Relax

Relax

52 brilliant little ideas to chill out

Elisabeth Wilson

brilliantideas

CAREFUL NOW

Your actions are your own responsibility and it's up to you to make sensible choices. The publishers and I are not prepared to accept any responsibility for any kind of harm or damage that comes to you from any decision you reach as a result of reading this book. If you're in any doubt about whether your ideas are safe, speak to an expert on the subject (if you're the litigious kind, find one who's got insurance cover). And don't do anything I wouldn't do.

First published in 2006 by
The Infinite Ideas Company Limited
36 St Giles
Oxford, OX1 3LD
United Kingdom
www.infideas.com

Reprinted 2007

A CIP catalogue record for this book is available from the British Library
ISBN 978-1-904902-39-3

Designed and typeset by Baseline Arts Ltd, Oxford
Printed in China

Brilliant ideas

Introduction

'Having it all' translates, as we know, into 'doing it all'. And as the roles we're gleefully supposed to inhabit grows we're 'being it all' too. Women are used to hearing how difficult it is to inhabit their multi-tasking, multi-role lives. But I'd hazard it's the same for men – not only have they got to be exemplary hunter-gatherers (even more so than previous generations), but they are also expected to be fabulous fathers, wonderful lovers and nice to their mums.

So we know stress is A Bad Thing. It leaches our energy and is the forerunner of just about every major illness going, and quite few minor ones too. And we know that the ability to relax is A Good Thing, but since you can't get it in pill form from your pharmacist and have to do it yourself, the relaxation thing causes quite a few problems for us, too. It's yet another thing to add to the to-do list. This book is for people who are constantly pressured and whom the usual advice doesn't ever hit. Let's face it, if you're the sort of person who enjoys doing an hour of yoga every morning and then soaking for an hour in a candle-lit bath every night, you probably don't need any advice on relaxing – this book is for the people who struggle to find time for a shower, much less a bath.

When you understand how stress impacts on your body, it's easy to take measures that disperse that stress pronto. You become better at nipping the stressors in the bud – just as you nip the chances of getting dysentery in the bud by choosing not to drink dirty, smelly water.

Stress will find you. You can't avoid it. You'll find ways of dealing with extreme stress here – the sort of stress that pole-axes your life. If stress has been creeping up on you gradually there are ways of defusing months' worth of stress in a few hours. But at the end of the day, stress is an active, not a passive pursuit. Studies have shown that most of us know how to relax but we can't be bothered to do it. So don't just read but act. Most of these ideas sound embarrassingly simple but they work on a profound level – if you do them. The only way that you can possibly become a more relaxed person is to do more that relaxes you and less that stresses you. Self-evident you might think, but not to all of us.

Stress is a fact of life. We can make some of it go away, we can ignore some of it, but eventually we will have to deal with it. Here are some ways of dealing with it simply...and fast.

1. Hug your home

It's hard to feel relaxed when your home is filthy. And even if it's clean, keeping it that way is often a major cause of anxiety.

Here are some ideas for relaxing housework. It will benefit two groups of people.

- The owner of a messy home – your house will be cleaner.
- The owner of an already immaculate home, but one who finds herself polishing kitchen units at midnight.

I urge anyone domestically challenged to seek out www.flylady.com. A bit hokey, but sweet, it's a support group for those who have felt overwhelmed by the ceaseless round of domestic duty and fed up struggling with it alone. They have rules. One of them is that the minute you get up, you make your bed, get dressed (including shoes), wash your face get your make-up on or shave. Try this and you'll be amazed at how much more productive you are. I have adapted some of their other rules to suit me.

Always have a clean kitchen sink

With a shiny sink, you feel you're in control. A shiny sink reflects back a vision of yourself as a domestic goddess (or god) in stunning

Here's an idea for you

When cooking, fill the sink with hot soapy water and dump stuff in as you go along. Yes, even if you have a dishwasher. It helps you keep surfaces clear and you enjoy yourself more, too.

control of your world. Don't leave home or go to bed for the night without clearing the sink area. It really is best to clear your kitchen straight after the evening meal – or get your kids to do it. Before bed you can't always be bothered and it sets the morning off to a bad start.

Adopt the laser beam approach

Divide your home section into clearly defined areas. You will clean one of these areas thoroughly every week. No area should take more than an hour. This could look like: hallway and bathroom; kitchen; reception rooms; bedroom and spare bedroom; children's bedroom(s). Now make a list of what you need to do to each area to get it cleaned to your satisfaction. Keep a master list for each room in a file. With a list you get to tick off items and that's immensely satisfying. First thing Saturday morning is a good time to clean, not least because if you have children they can get involved.

Bless your home

This is the superficial cleaning you do to keep your home bearable. It takes an hour a week – or you can split it up. I do 10 minutes morning and evening, three times a week. That on top of the hour a week I spend on one area is usually enough to keep my (small) home bearable. You may have a larger home and need to put more time in.

2. Grumpy old git – or really, really sick?

If you're a man and you're angry, could it be your hormones that are to blame?

Depression, anger, anxiety, fatigue, moodiness and low libido – our men are facing a crisis of some sort whatever the reason – hormonal or otherwise. Increasing pressure to maintain a career and increasing demands from women to be more equal partners are the biggest culprits. No wonder men are in a constant state of tension.

What helps?

When you find it hard to talk

Very many men aren't great at talking through their feelings. Jed Diamond recommends going for a walk as men are better at communication when side by side than face to face. Or you could try going for a drive. The enclosed space allows for uninterrupted chat, and the lack of eye contact takes the pressure off.

When you're permanently down

Eventually if you want to stop being irritable, you have to find your way back through rediscovering your passion for life. Let's hope it's not

Here's an idea for you

Stay off the cigs, and get off them if possible. If you smoke, you're not helping yourself. Smoke doesn't relax you – in fact it causes you to get hyped up. (Think what you'd do if you were having a fag and your boss stormed through the door in a rage with you. No, you wouldn't keep smoking.) Give up but get support. A recent study has discovered that people who were sent encouraging texts from loved ones intermittently through the day found it much easier to quit.

for your secretary. If you're struggling to find a reason to get out of bed in the morning, much less find your passion, start small. The important thing is action. Think of one goal you'd like to achieve that would make you feel good – a small goal is fine. Make a list of what you need to do to achieve it. Start working towards happiness as you would towards any other goal.

When you spend your time glued to the TV

Professor John McKinley, a top US researcher into the male menopause, is convinced most of the symptoms are due to being overweight, drinking too much and being inactive. Depression may be in the mix somewhere. TV or any other distracting behaviours are just a way of avoiding the fact that you're mental and physical health are shot. Harsh words. But try losing ten kilos and doing some exercise – that will help your health and mood immensely.

3. Life–work balance

I refuse to call it work–life. It should be life–work.

One of the most pernicious things about stress is the way we don't notice how it switches our attention away from what we value and love in life until it's too late. So here are some clues to work out if tension is stomping all over your life–work balance...

- Do you feel like your day is spent dealing with difficult people and difficult tasks?
- Do you feel that those you love don't have a clue what's going on with you and you don't have a clue what's going on with them?
- Do you regularly make time for activities that nourish your soul?
- Do you feel you could leave home and no one would notice you were gone until the mortgage had to be paid?

Number 3 was the trick question. Answer yes to that one and you're probably all right. Answer yes to the rest and you could be in trouble.

Here's an idea for you

Designate Saturday 'family' day and Sunday afternoon 'selfish' time. We can usually find an hour or so on Sunday afternoon to spend on ourselves – just don't let it get filled with chores or your partner's agenda.

17

In a nutshell: make sure you're putting time and effort into the people and activities that make your heart sing and it really is very difficult to buckle under the effect of constant worry. But I think too much emphasis is put on the anxiety caused by the 'work' part of the equation and not enough placed on the anxiety caused by the 'life' bit. Everyone assumes that all we need is less work, more life and all would be harmonious balance. Hmmm.

Where it has gone all wrong for so many, women especially, is that they've cleared enough time for the 'life' part of the equation but not taken into account that it isn't necessarily restful or enjoyable. This is no idle observation. Research shows that men's stress hormones tend to fall when they get home whereas women's stay high after the working day, presumably because they get home to confront a dozen chores and hungry kids. Your children may be the reason you get out of bed in the morning but you need to accept that spending time with them is not necessarily any less stressful than work – in fact, it often makes work seem like a walk in the park. More time with your kids is not necessarily the answer.

More time with yourself, very probably, is – if you don't look after yourself, you can't look after anyone else. And it takes just ten minutes a day.

4. On your bike?

Only one thing gets you down, and hence stressed, more than work. Not working.

Paradoxically, one of the most stressed periods of any life is when you don't have to worry about the nine-to-five because for whatever reason you're no longer in paid employment.

People in low-paid, menial jobs are far more anxious than thrusting Type A folk. They have little control over their working life and there's nothing less relaxing than lack of control. Those made redundant or who are 'between jobs', women who have had children and opted to stay at home – anyone basically who doesn't get paid (note, I didn't say who doesn't work) is vulnerable to the tension of the 'no work' phenomenon. So what's the answer?

If you're looking for a job, don't fritter away time worrying while making half-hearted or piecemeal attempts to find one. You need a strategy. You need short-term and long-term goals. You need to break these goals down into tasks and you need to schedule these tasks in your diary. When you're anxious it's a lot easier to spend hours fine-tuning your CV and waiting for the phone to ring than being proactive.

Ask five people that know you well to answer these questions honestly

- What is the first thing you think of when you think of me?
- What do you think is the most interesting thing about me?
- What do you think has been my greatest accomplishment?
- What do you value most about me?
- What do you perceive to be my greatest strengths?

OK. A bit embarrassing. But just say you've been asked to answer these questions on a job application and you're (becomingly modestly) stuck for ideas. What you'll be amazed at is the different perceptions people have of you. It also helps you realise that qualities you take for granted aren't qualities that everyone shares. You're unique.

When you're short of money, isolated and bored, it's unlikely that you're getting the regular doses of endorphins that we need to stay happy campers. Understimulation leads to fatigue and depression. It's essential to manufacture highs and you have to do it daily. Make a 'joy list' of things that will give you a sense of achievement and happiness that don't cost a lot. By slotting them regularly into your day, you'll fire off endorphins and fool your body that you are still a high-flyer with endless cash to fritter away on life's inanities. You could decide to start every day with an alfresco breakfast, spend an afternoon watching a movie or have a glass of wine under the stars. Every day must have one pure pleasure.

5. Let's get positive

So you're stressed? Be grateful. Stress makes life a lot sweeter when you learn to manage it right.

Some stress is good. Some stress is necessary. When you're stressed your adrenal glands produce a hormone called dehydroepiandrosterone – known as DHEA to its friends – which has been shown to keep mice alive longer. It was also noted that the same mice had more luxuriant coats. The hormone is thought to build collagen and elastin (the building bricks of the skin) and this stimulates a younger looking appearance. (The beauty industry has latched onto this and is trying to develop products that contain DHEA. You're ahead of your game, you produce your own.)

DHEA makes your mind sharper. Chronic stress makes you forgetful but short-term stress can make your brain work better for short periods.

Here's an idea for you

Relaxation is easier in the dark. Anytime you need to relax instantly, put your palms over your eyes, shut them and imagine you are enveloped in black velvet.

If you're feeling down in the dumps, a bit of stress isn't necessarily terrible. It could be just what you need to perk you up again. Stress forces you to make decisions and take responsibility. Experts believe this protects us from falling into a state of depression. A recent study found that short doses of the stress hormone cortisol protects some people against depression in the way that anti-depressants regulate mood. Too much cortisol leads to extreme exhaustion, but just a little bit is fine.

Let's hear it for our old friend, DHEA. Women with a low libido who were given doses of DHEA got more interested again. It turns out that low levels of stress is linked to control of sex drive. Moderate stress releases DHEA and this affects libido positively.

A study carried out at the University of Texas showed that people with few pressures are up to 50% more likely to die within ten years of quitting work than those who faced major responsibility. People under regular pressure tend to take better control of their lives and as a result suffer fewer conditions linked to failing finances, poor relationships and employment problems.

Life is innately stressful. Even if you lock yourself in your bedroom for the foreseeable future, stress will find you out. Stress is caused by change, and life changes even if you withdraw from it and hide under the bed. But by learning to manage stress, and use it to your advantage, you can find it motivates, energises and spurs you on to a richer and more fulfilling life. And read this idea whenever it's getting you down. Remember there's only one thing worse for you than too much stress, and that's too little.

6. Restoration day

When you're suffering from chronic, long-term strain, when your batteries are blown, when burnout is imminent, here is your emergency plan.

The restoration day is based on three principles:

- Replenishing your body by giving it rest.
- Resting your brain by focusing on your body.
- Nourishing your soul with healthy simple food which will replenish the nutrients stripped away by anxiety.

When you wake, acknowledge that this day will be different. Today you are going to shift the emphasis onto relaxation and releasing tension and replacing what stress has drained away from your body.

Here's an idea for you

Go to bed at 9.30 p.m. today and every day this week if you can manage it. Don't watch TV if you're not tired – read or listen to music. People who do this have turned around their stress levels in a week.

Stretch. If you feel like it, turn over and go back to sleep. If not, read an inspirational tome – a self-help book, poetry, a favourite novel. Don't reach for your usual coffee or tea. Sip a mug of hot water with lemon: this, according to naturopaths, boosts the liver which has to work incredibly hard processing all the junk that goes into your body. Every time panic hits because you're not doing anything – now and for the rest of the day – breathe in deeply for a count of eight and out for a count of eight.

When you rise try to stretch every muscle in your body. Feel the cricks draining out. Try a fruit smoothie for breakfast: blend a cup of natural yogurt with one banana and a couple of handfuls of other fruits; peach, mango, strawberries, pineapple. Thin, if preferred, with a little fruit juice. Sip slowly, preferably outside. Today eat lightly and avoid (except for the odd treat) foods that strain digestion too much. Drink coffee and tea if you normally do; the last thing you want is a caffeine withdrawal headache. But don't have more than say three caffeine drinks.

Get outside – in the most natural surroundings you can manage. Ideally, lie on your back on the grass. Stare at the sky. Let your mind drift off. Or walk in the countryside, the park, sit in your garden. If you really can't bear to be still, do some gardening.

Have a huge salad combining every colour of vegetable you can think of – green, yellow, orange, purple, red for lunch. This meal must include one absolute treat – a glass of wine, a dish of ice-cream, a piece of chocolate. Lie back. Indulge.

Go back to bed after lunch, or curl up on a cosy corner of your sofa. Watch a favourite movie, or a comedy show. Sleep if you can. Or if you'd prefer, listen to some favourite music.

For dinner eat another pile of vegetables – a salad or perhaps a stir-fry, following the 'eat a rainbow' advice given above. Have a fresh piece of fish grilled or lightly fried Present your food beautifully; eat it by candlelight. Go to bed early. Resist the temptation to watch TV. Read a book, listen to the radio or some music.

7. Eat for health

Let your diet support you in your battle to relax. Lose weight, think clearly, sleep better. All this can be yours with food combining.

Here's an idea for you

Try to cut back on alcohol, artificially sweetened food, coffee, tea, soft drinks, margarine-type spreads, sugary foods and drinks. These all put a strain on the body and you're trying to minimise this.

Food combining is probably one of the most successful diets of all time. In a nutshell, it advocates never mixing concentrated protein and concentrated starch at the same meal. One group is acid forming, it's claimed, one alkaline. Mixing them puts strain on the digestive system and stops us reaching optimum health.

Unmitigated nonsense, most doctors will tell you. But then there are thousands of people who swear that food combining removes grumbling health problems and helps them think clearly, lose weight effortlessly and stay calm. I think that food combining is an excellent way to improve your level of nourishment and that's got to be good for your anxiety levels. It's almost impossible to experiment with it even on a part-time basis without improving your diet. Partly because it's near impossible to eat processed foods and the less processed food you eat, the healthier you get. Here are some basic principles. Try one or two – or all of them – and see if they work for you.

■ Don't combine concentrated proteins with concentrated starches at the same meal. Vegetables can be eaten with either protein or starches, as can a small amount of nuts. Fats and oils can be eaten with either. Stick to good-quality ones – organic butter, cold pressed olive oil.

- Eat fruit only on an empty stomach – several pieces for breakfast, or as a mid-afternoon snack, or as a starter before a meal. Fruit eaten with other foods can contribute to gas and bloating.
- Introduce a small green salad as a starter to your main meal.
- Eat pudding or fruit an hour after finishing your meal if at all possible. Sugar foods interfere with stomach acid and affect the transit of the rest of your meal.
- Start slowly. Eat one food combining meal for two days each week and gradually up the numbers.
- Don't get too hung up on it. Work in broad categories. It's not the end of the world if you mix a little protein with carbohydrate. Rice, for instance, is predominantly carbohydrate but does contain a little protein. Most foods are a mixture (which is where food combining critics have a field day). But the idea is to get the big picture and categorise foods according to the main group that they fall into.

8. The perfection trap

Your need to 'get it perfect' isn't about perfection. It's about staying in control.

I have a friend who looks better than me, earns more than me, achieves more than me,

Here's an idea for you

but a small voice inside constantly tells her that she's just not good enough. Does it have to be that way? I think perfectionists can achieve just as much if they let that voice go for good.

Only you can learn to ignore the little voice. If you don't, you'll never be able to relax properly. Often that little voice belongs to someone we know, often someone who brought us up, who has no ideas of the complexity of our world. Give it up!

- Ration your perfectionist behaviour. You probably won't ever lose it completely. However, you can limit it. One woman I know whose energy levels had plummeted finally made the connection between her habit of staying up late reading and answering emails and her inability to get to sleep (duh!). So now she allows herself two nights a week to check emails late. Go through your own life working out where you can cut down or cut out perfectionist habits.
- Lose your fear of the person who made you this way. Even if you were always the sort of kid who liked to colour code your books, no one becomes a perfectionist unaided. Someone somewhere had high expectations of you. Accept something pretty basic: if you haven't earned their unconditional approval by now, you probably never will. Let it go. And if you can't, get therapy.

- Walk barefoot in the park. Remember Jane Fonda begging Robert Redford to stop being such a stuffed shirt and to walk barefoot in Central Park. You could try the same – just to see if you like it. You probably won't but it might teach you something valuable: that nobody cares but you. Whatever your version of mad devil-may-care spontaneity – asking friends to dinner and ordering a takeaway curry, or letting your roots show, or putting on a few kilos, or refusing to take the kids swimming on Sunday morning because you simply can't be fagged – go on do it. The kids will not implode with disappointment. The world will not fall apart. Slip up and nothing happens.

No one cares if you're perfect but you (and the person who made you this way, see above, but we've dealt with them already).

9. A zone of your own

Imagine a place with no phone, no noise, no hassle, no problems.

Having a place you can call your own helps immeasurably with relaxation. I realised this on reading a book of sacred and meditation rooms around the world. The need for a quiet place is universal. I was intrigued by the ingenuity of those

Here's an idea for you

Write down what taste, scent, sensation, sound and sight immediately relaxes you and gather them in one place so they are always at hand. Velvet slippers, satin quilts, birdsong, pink light, roses. What sensual cues calm you down instantly.

who clearly lived in the real world like me, where knocking out the centre of the house to build an atrium wasn't really an option. One woman had turned a fair-sized cupboard into her own sanctuary and filled it with objects significant to her. I was particularly taken by a sweet Sikh who kept his shrine on a breakfast tray and simply stuck it in a cupboard when it wasn't being used. (It was beautiful, too.)

Why bother? Because I think that in some very profound way having a corner where you can let your imagination run free and where you have control is deeply important to the human spirit. As a child did you have a secret place where you would hide away? Did you build 'shrines'? No? Think of the times you set up your favourite toys next to your bed, your dolls aligned looking just right on a shelf, 'special' power stones hidden in a secret place only you knew about? Children love talismans and can spend hours contemplating a feather, a flower, a broken bottle. This is how they relax away from their parents, in a world of their own where they choose objects that soothe them and where they decide their significance – not the grown ups.

Creating a place where you can go that is uniquely yours, where you have chosen what you look at, what you feel, hear and smell will prove invaluable in your battle against tension. A room is ideal, a cupboard will do, a corner of a room – just one armchair will be enough. There you are in control and you can read, rest, dream, just be. It could be a seat in your garden, a daybed in the spare room, a dressing table, or simply a shelf or windowsill on which a simple cerulean vase holding a pink rose sits. But it should be so attractive to you that you long to sink into your sanctuary – that way you'll want to carve out a little time for yourself as often as possible so you can be there. And that's the essence of relaxation.

10. Find an hour a day to play

No seriously, is that too much to ask?

We can view the 'desirable' things we'd like to spend an hour doing in two categories:

■ The stuff we yearn to do because it's relaxing and fun.
■ The stuff that's usually prefixed with a sense of 'ought to' because we know the rewards are worth it

Here's an idea for you

On the move and pressured? Running cold water over your wrists for a minute cools you down on a hot day and it works to bring down your anxiety levels, too.

We need to find the time for both. But both categories tend to get shunted to the sidelines of our life because of general business. Nothing in your life will change unless you take action. If you don't take the time to exercise, if you consistently allow family and work demands to be more important than your continual good health, then at best you'll be more vulnerable to illness; at worst you'll be fat (and still more vulnerable to illness).

This goes for 'life dreams' that fall into the first category, like writing a novel or learning Russian. These have been called 'depth activities' because they add meaning to our lives. Here's the big question: how will you feel in five years' time if you haven't at least tried to achieve one of your dreams?

First get the big picture. Get out your diary and write down everything you're expected to make happen in the next month. This could take some time. Include everything from work projects, organising baby-sitters, buying birthday presents, decorating the bathroom, taxing the car, medical appointments.

Now go through the list and mark the items that you can delegate to someone else. Be honest. Items you can delegate, not the ones that no one else wants to do, or the ones that no one else will do as well as you.

Don't worry. You don't have to hand over all these tasks, just 10% of them.

Now you've offloaded 10% of your work for the next month, think about dumping 10% of what you have to do every day. Jot down your 'tasks' for tomorrow. Quickly, without thinking too much, run through them marking each entry: **A** Must do; **B** Should do; **C** Could do

Now knock two of the Bs and three of the Cs off the list and put down in their place an activity that you know would relax you or add depth to your life. Mark it with a whacking great 'A'. Life really is too short to wallow in the C-list – feeling busy but achieving nothing that matters.

11. Crisis management

Facing the week from hell? Here's how to survive it.

On really busy days with multiple deadlines, I've got to the stage where I'm scared to answer the phone in case it's someone demanding something else of me. Then I made a conscious decision

Here's an idea for you

to stop being a victim. Every time a negative thought crosses your brain, cancel it out with a positive one. This takes practice. An easy way to do it is to develop a mantra to suit whatever crisis you're in today and that you say to yourself mindlessly every time your mind goes into tailspin. Right now, I have to pick the kids up from school in half an hour. I have four weeks to my deadline for this book and I have done approximately half the number of words I promised myself I'd write today. My mantra is 'I am serenely gliding towards my deadline and everything will get done' and every time panic hits, I chant this to myself and feel much better.

The 'best use' question was taught to me by my first boss and it is invaluable in negotiating your way through any day with dozens of calls on your time. It helps you to prioritise 'on the run', sometimes quite ruthlessly. On the morning of manic days decide what you've got to achieve that day and if anything interrupts, ask yourself 'Is this the best use of my time, right now?' If the answer's no, take a rain-check and come back to it later. So if a friend calls at work, nine times out of ten, you won't chat then, you'll call her back at a more convenient time – unless, of course, she is very upset about something, then talking to her is the best use of your time.

A lot of hassle is of our own making. Life coach Thomas Leonard says, 'One of the biggest mistakes is to tell people what they want to hear, give them what they think they want, without thinking if it's feasible for you. You overpromise results you can't deliver without a lot of stress. And of course, if you don't deliver, not only are you stressed, they are, too.' Leonard's advice is to underpromise rather than overpromise. That way your friends are delighted when you turn up at the party you said you couldn't make and your boss thinks you're wonderful when you get the report finished a day early rather than a week late. Make it your rule from now on to be absolutely realistic about how long it's going to take you to get things done. And until you get expert at this, work out the time you reckon it will take you to complete any task and multiply it by 1.5.

12. Relax for Christmas

This year, let's make it different. No hassle, no worry. Honest!

One survey discovered that we rate Christmas as one of the most stressful life events just after moving house, changing jobs and divorce. Two-thirds of us are mentally and physically drained after Christmas.

Here's an idea for you

Get the worry out of your head and on the page. Buy a beautiful notebook and keep it with you at all times from November on. Scribble down ideas for presents, stray thoughts about the menu, addresses of friends for cards, baby-sitter numbers...anything you'll need.

So to avoid 'crash and burn', try this countdown. This is the *crème de la crème* of the tips that worked for me.

Start early

For me, Christmas cards were always a complete chore, not to say bore. But then I started following the advice of a friend. She has an old box covered in Christmas paper and each year she fills it with Christmas cards and stamps. It stays on the kitchen table all through November and she sits down most evenings, puts on some nice music, pours a huge glass of wine and gets stuck in. Five cards a night takes 20 minutes.

The one-day shopping blitz

I spend one day shopping for my family and one day shopping for everyone else. I have a good idea what I'm buying for my family so it's not too difficult. For everyone else I do it in one day, in one store. To make this fun, go with a friend. Take a day off work and meet in the best department store in town for breakfast. Then at 10 a.m. sharp spend three hours shopping and meet again for lunch in the store's restaurant. Then split up for another two hours and meet up for afternoon tea. Finally, split up again and meet for cocktails in the bar across the road at 6 p.m. You can adapt this idea to suit yourself and your environment. If you do everything by the internet, allow yourself just one day to do everything. This method focuses the mind. You have to make decisions quickly.

The cut-off point
For me Christmas Eve is about missing the last-minute rush. I like to take the day off, build a big log fire, listen to carols on the radio and heat up some mince pies so the smell wafts through the house. Pretend I'm a domestic goddess for just one day, basically.

But if you have to rush around, or even like to rush around, at least give yourself a cut-off point after which you down tools, pour yourself a glass of something bubbly and take an hour or so to admire your tree piled high with presents. The end-point focuses you and, funnily enough, you'll get it done by then.

13. A shortcut to coping with obstacles

For every behaviour or action, there's a payback. When you work out the payback you often drain away a lot of tension from a situation.

These are some of the random (cruel) thoughts that have crossed my mind during conversations with friends and acquaintances in the last couple of months.

- If you're over 35 and still trying to please your mother, it's time you stopped, not least because acting like a child isn't going to advance your chances of ever having a half-decent relationship with her.
- If you're a man (or, indeed, woman) who uses work as an escape route to get out of going home, it's pretty obvious to everyone what's going on, including the folks back home. Maybe that's why your family are so darned unpleasant when you bother to show up?
- If you're feeling awful because you've had an affair, you deserve to. Not for the mindless sex but for neglecting your primary relationship in the first place. You were too cowardly to address the problems and are too cowardly now, having precipitated a crisis instead in order to force your spouse to make decisions.

Here's an idea for you

Write down three situations in the last week that have freaked you out. Then work out what the payback was. Make a game out of working out the payback for your actions on a daily basis. It's interesting to observe when you're 'running a racket' (which is life coach speak for kidding yourself).

Remember I didn't actually say these things. These people were distressed and the last thing a distressed person needs is a know-it-all. However, if we were really serious about sorting out our problems, we could start by taking our share of the responsibility for creating them.

When you realise the great truth that you create a lot of your anxiety by your choices, then you're in a position to work out the payback – your 'reward', what you're getting from the situation. And I guarantee that there will always be a payback. Sometimes the payback is worth the angst. You choose to look after your ill child. Nothing could be more worrying. The payback is, of course, self-evident.

Others are more tricky. Sacked from your job? But remember, you decided to stay when the company started looking dodgy because the pay was good. Being chased by the taxman? Hmmm, you did wonder why your tax bill seemed low, but weren't concerned enough to double-check your accountant's figures.

Just by recognising that in every single thing you do, every single relationship you have, every single habit you have, you are getting some sort of payback or you wouldn't do it is incredibly liberating. Once we're self-aware we tend to change of our own free will. The truth will set you free. Honest.

14. Relaxation – learn from the cavemen

There's nothing wrong with stress. We're designed to get stressed. It's how we deal with it that's the problem.

Stress developed in order for us to deal with danger. When faced with something that scares us we release adrenaline, which in turn causes the release of noradrenaline and cortisol and these three hormones together sharpen our wits, release energy to our muscles and divert resources from one part of the body to the bits where you need it most. Which is why you feel twitchy when you're very stressed and can't sit still. The adrenaline coursing through your body would have been just dandy in helping you cope with a sabre-toothed tiger but is a bit of an overreaction when your boss has caught you booking your holiday on the internet rather than working on the sales report. All those hormones get the job done. But rest is essential to repair and recover from their effect.

So what do we do now after a difficult day? We are likeliest to celebrate with alcohol, a cigarette, coffee (all of which trigger another stress response). Or even worse, after a stressful situation, we throw ourselves straight into another one. This means that our bodies are bathed in stress hormones for far longer than was ever intended.

The body's hormones work in delicate balance. When the three main stress hormones are fired they affect the levels of all the others, notably insulin (which regulates sugar levels and energy) and serotonin (the happy hormone which affects mood and sleep). When they go awry over long periods of time, the results can be disastrous for our health, both mental and physical.

See your day not as a long purgatory of angst but as lots of small stress responses punctuated with mini-relaxation breaks. As a rough rule, every waking hour should have five minutes of pleasure. So after every hour of working, take a few moments to do something pleasurable – answer an email, stretch your shoulders, have a cup of tea. Can't leave your desk? Spend a few minutes dreaming of something that makes you happy.

Fifteen minutes every day practise active relaxation – listening to music, yoga, sex, dancing. TV is passive and doesn't count.

At least three hours every week should be spent doing an activity you love. It should be calming, and non-work orientated. I make it a rule that it only counts as my three hours if I can do it without

Here's an idea for you

Next time you're waiting in a queue, or for traffic lights to change or for the lift to come, see it as an opportunity for a mini-break. Take some deep breaths, feel the tension flow out of your body and your shoulders drop. People who make an effort to do this report being more positive in a week.

make-up. In other words, it doesn't count if it involves people that I feel I have to make an effort with.

15. Just say no

Cure yourself of the disease to please.

Now and then, all of us have to do things that don't benefit us much in order to feel that we're pulling our weight. But if it's a daily occurrence then we're going to get run down, ill and seriously fed up. Try this quiz. Answer True or False for each of these questions:

- I can't relax until I finish all the things I have to do.
- If I wasn't doing favours for other people most days, I wouldn't think much of myself.
- I seldom say no to a work colleague or family member who asks a favour of me.
- I often find myself changing my own plans or working day to fit in with other people's wants.
- I rarely, if ever, feel comfortable with what I've accomplished.
- I often feel I'm so exhausted that I don't have time for my own interests.
- I feel guilty relaxing.

- I find myself saying 'yes' to others and inside a voice is saying 'no, no, no'.
- I honestly believe that if I stop doing things for others they'd think less of me.
- I find it hard to ask other people to do things for me.

Here's an idea for you

If you just can't say no, try an intermediate stage. Next time someone asks you to do something, say: 'I'm not sure, let me get back to you.' The breather is often enough to stiffen your resolve.

Add up the number of Ts you scored. If your score is between 7 and 10, you think it more important to please others than please yourself. If it's between 4 and 6, you should be careful. You're on the slippery slope to terminal niceness. If your score is 3 or less, you're good at saying no and keep your own needs in balance with others.

Aim for a score of under 3. Here are some ways to get there.

1. List your top 10 'no's, the things you want to eliminate from your life. Start each sentence 'I will no longer…'
2. Think of situations where you need to say no to improve your life. Imagine yourself in these situations saying no. Practise the exercise in front of a mirror if necessary. (This is brilliant. The experience of actually saying no out loud, albeit in private, makes it much easier in real-life situations.)
3. Whenever you're asked to do anything, ask yourself: 'Do I really want to do this?' rather than 'Should I do this?' If the answer is no, then let someone else pick up the baton.

16. Turning Japanese

Try this and you'll see why the Japanese consider having a bath a sacred experience.

The Japanese bath has cumulative effects – the more often you do it, the more powerfully it works. There is a set pattern to it and the predictability in itself is soothing. You will need: a balancing essential oil such as lavender or geranium or frankincense, an aromatherapy burner, a quiet place to sit, a clean bathroom (free of clutter), some soft towels (preferably warmed), a loofah or a body brush or sisal glove, a small bowl, comfortable clothes, a teapot, cup, strainer, loose-leafed tea, a candle, a blanket, and a minimum of one hour.

First, light the burner in the bathroom, lock the door and sit there quietly breathing in the fragrance, letting your mind quieten and be still. Lay your hands on your stomach, breathe in deeply and feel your stomach move out. Breathe out and feel your stomach contracting. Let go of all other thoughts. Now, and for the rest of this hour, keep your focus on what you can see, feel, hear and smell. Anxious thoughts will intrude, of course. When they do, imagine them drifting off in the fragrance rising from the burner.

When you're relaxed, undress and gently draw a brush or loofah over your body, working always towards the heart. Then step into the shower – it works best if it is at a slightly cooler temperature than usual. Lather up and get really clean. Concentrate on the noise of the shower. Let anxious thoughts disappear down the plughole with the soapy water.

Clean? Now step out the shower and run yourself a hot bath. Add a few drops of your balancing oil to the rushing water. Sink into the bath. When intrusive worrying thoughts interrupt, let them gently float away in the steam. When you're good and chilled out use the small bowl to ladle water all over your body. The idea is not to get clean but to focus your mind on pouring the water as gracefully as possible. Study the pattern of the falling water. Let yourself enter a sort of trance state, soothed by the repetitive actions. When thoughts of the outside world intrude, imagine them moving from your mind to being plastered on your body and then visualise them being swept away by the falling water.

When your mind is calm and you feel centred, emerge, wrap yourself in warm towels, dry off and dress in warm, comfortable clothing. Hold this 'mindful' state. Go to a peaceful corner of your home and

Here's an idea for you

Invest in some special props that you keep purely for restoration. The sense of 'specialness' helps turn a bath into an event and with time you will be able to trigger relaxation with just part of the ritual. A cup of tea, a bath with the balancing oil or body brushing will in themselves be almost as good as the whole ritual.

light a candle. (If you can do this whole ritual by candlelight, it will be even more restful). Then make some tea, concentrating fully on every step. Watch the kettle boil, relax and breathe deeply and keep your mind as restful as possible. Make your movements as graceful and economical as possible.

Green tea gives the authentic 'Eastern' feeling. Herbal is good. But any tea will do. Finally, retire to your quiet place, cosy up with a blanket, sip your tea, inhale the fragrance, focus on the candle flame, keep your attention on it. Concentrate on the taste of the tea. Imagine anxious thoughts drifting away in the fragrant steam rising from your cup.

17. Are you too stressed to be happy?

Stress saps energy and eventually our enjoyment of life. Stress makes us unhappy without us even realising it.

The World Health Organisation's definition of good health is not just an absence of disease but the 'presence of emotional and physical well-being'. So are you healthy? Few of us can remember when we last felt 100% emotionally and physically well. And the chances are that it's stress that's bringing you down.

Here are some questions to help you pinpoint how worry is affecting your well-being, perhaps without you realising it.

Stage 1

Do you have a sense of injustice or resentment against people you don't know such as big lottery winners or acquaintances who seem to have a much better life than you?
Do you say 'should', 'ought to', 'must' a lot?
Are minor niggles with neighbours or colleagues dominating your thinking?

Stage 2

Do you feel guilty about being unhappy with your life?
Do you find it hard to motivate yourself?
Do you feel tired all the time?
Do you lack confidence and self-esteem?

Stage 3

Have you had repeated problems for a prolonged period of time?
Do you have trouble remembering the last time you really laughed out loud?
Are the people around you a constant source of disappointment?
Do you think that life could be so much better if you could only

Here's an idea for you

Lemon balm helps beat anxiety and irritability. You can buy lemon balm herb in supplement form at your chemist or find a supplier on the web.

resolve one negative issue?
Do you suffer from constant anxiety?
Do you think it is impossible to improve your situation?

If you ticked any statements in stage 1, you'll benefit from finding more pleasure in the life you've got – seeking out good feelings like a pleasure-seeking missile will make a huge difference to your state of mind.

If you ticked any in stage 2, stress is having a serious effect on your mood and could be pushing you into depression. Read on, but consider talking to your doctor.

If you ticked stage 3 it's time to consult your doctor. You might benefit from counselling. When repetitive thought patterns or overwhelming anxiety are making life miserable, you might want to consider cognitive behavioural therapy which is designed to work in a matter of weeks.

18. Stress is other people

Here's how to deal with the energy black holes.

All around you are the energy black holes, people who are unhappy, negative or angry and who would like nothing more than to drag you into their miserable world. And there is absolutely nothing you can do about them. The only thing you can change is your attitude. But sometimes, even most times, it's not you – it's them.

Other people have their own agenda. You can't know what it is and you can't change it. Take a tip from Rosamond Richardson, author and yoga teacher. She recommends visualising yourself surrounded by white light, creating a protective bubble around you. Negativity just bounces off this white light and can't affect you. Sounds nuts, but it works. Try it and see.

Don't waste a moment dwelling on how much better life would be if John would only be kinder, Mum would cheer up a bit, Emily was more help around the home, or your boss was less aggressive.

This is a surprisingly telling little exercise that you can do in five minutes on the back of a napkin. It may give you shock. Make a list of the people with whom you have regular contact. Then divide that list into three categories:

- *The energisers* They look after you in every way. They give great advice. They bring happiness to your life.
- *The neutral* They're OK. Neither great nor bad.
- *The drainers* They're users, people who don't deliver, let you down, bring you down. They also include gossips, people whose conversation is sexist or racist, and bitchy, sarcastic types whose conversation, no matter how entertaining, makes you feel bad about yourself afterwards.

And you know what I'm going to say. Maximise time with the energisers. Look for them when you enter a room and gravitate towards them whether you've been introduced or not. We all know these people when we meet them. If you have too many neutrals, think how you can bring more energisers into your life.

Here's an idea for you

A lot of strain in our relationships with other people comes from trying to second guess what they're thinking or what their intention is. Try saying: 'What other people think of me is none of my business.' Think about that statement closely. When you start believing it, life gets a whole lot easier.

And the drainers? Your time with them should be strictly limited. And if some of them are your closest friends, your family, your lover, you need to think about that very carefully. You may feel unable to cut them out now (although that is an option) but you can limit the time they are allowed to suck you into their world.

19. Leave the office on time

Reduce interruptions. Reclaim your evenings.

Don't be a slave to a daily 'to-do' list. See the big picture. On Monday morning lose the sinking 'I've got so much to do' sensation. Instead, think 'What are my goals for this week?' Decide what you want to have done by Friday and then break each goal into smaller tasks that have to be undertaken to achieve all you want by Friday. Slot these tasks in throughout your week. This helps you prioritise so that the tricky and difficult things, or tasks that depend on other people's input, don't sink to the back of your consciousness. It also means you are giving attention to all that you have to do and not spending too much time on one task at the beginning of the week. Concentrate on three or four items on your 'to-do' list at once. You won't be overwhelmed.

Some of us operate better in the morning, some in the late afternoon. If your job demands creativity, block out your most creative periods so that you can concentrate on your projects. Don't allow them to be impinged upon by meetings and phone calls that could be done anytime.

Here's an idea for you

Create a 'virtual you' if you're getting hassled in the office by the demands of others. When you're an administrative lynchpin, set up a shared file where people can go to find the information or resources they'd usually get from you.

Make the phone call you're dreading Right now. That call that saps your energy all day. Just do it.

Have meetings in the morning People are frisky. They want to whizz through stuff and get on with their day. Morning meetings go much faster than those scheduled in the afternoon.

Check emails three times a day First thing in the morning, just after lunch and just before you leave are ideal times. Keeping to this discipline means that you don't use email as a distraction.

Limit phone calls Talk to other people when it suits you, not them. Limit your calls as you do your emails – to three times a day. Make a list of calls you have to make that day. Call first thing. If someone isn't there, leave a message and unless you have to talk to them urgently, ask them to call you back at your next 'phone period'. Just before lunch or around 4.30pm is good. That means neither of you will linger over the call. Of course, you can't limit phone calls completely to these times but most of us have some control over incoming calls.

20. Never procrastinate again

Procrastination is worry's best friend. It's not big, it's not clever but for most of us, it's a way of life.

But no longer. Here is the best method for overcoming it, here's how to get straight to the point, no beating about the bush or going round the houses. It's Mark Foster's rotation method from his brilliant book *Get Everything Done*. Mark calls this the rotation method. You need pen, paper and a watch but a kitchen timer with a bell works best.

1. First make a list of your tasks. (Here is my list for this morning: write two ideas for this book, organise dinner party, do washing, make phone calls to pay some bills.)
2. Against each item write 10, 20, 30. These represent blocks of minutes that you are going to spend on each item in turn. So my list would look like:

   Write book 10, 20, 30
   Organise party 10, 20, 30
   Laundry 10, 20, 30
   Pay bills 10, 20, 30
3. Start with the task that puts you off least. Set the timer for 10

minutes. Do the task for 10 minutes. (I have my load of laundry on comfortably within the 10 minutes.)

4. When the timer rings. Stop. Wherever you are in the task. Stop. Score through the 10 next to the task.

5. Set the timer for 10 minutes. Start the next task. (It takes me the whole 10 minutes to get the paraphernalia together to pay the bills.

6. Score through the 10 on the list and start next task (Writing. The task that is most formidable, but buoyed on by the fact that I've made a start on the mundane tasks, I sit down make some notes and start typing.

7. Score off 10 and start next task. (I look through recipe books for 10 minutes and make some notes on whom to invite.)

8. Score off 10 minutes. Now move onto the first task again but set the timer for 20 minutes. Repeat the entire process. The next load of laundry takes 10 minutes but I score off the 20 next to laundry as there's nothing more I can do. I set the timer to 20 minutes for the bills. I am halfway through paying the last bill when the timer goes. Score off 20. I move back to the writing with a sense of relief – that's the job that's most important and because of my 10-minute start I'm raring to go. When the timer goes after 20 minutes, I go back to the party, finalise the guest list and decide on the menu. Back to the laundry – 30 minutes. This takes much less than 30 minutes. Now I go back to my computer and complete another 30 minutes. After 30 minutes I pause and look at my list. All the chores have been completed. I'm where I

want to be – sitting at my computer and enjoying writing, so I set my timer for 40 minutes and carry on, promising myself a cup of tea at the end. I'm so into it after 40 minutes that I bring the cup of tea back to my desk and carry on until lunch time.

Here's an idea for you

Scan your diary for big projects coming up. Tomorrow spend just 10 minutes working on each project. By giving a tiny amount of focused attention regularly to projects, well in advance, you accomplish them without even noticing.

This method works. I promise.

21. Learn to bounce

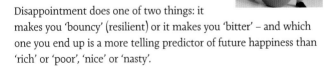

How come some people are better at dealing with disappointment than others?

Disappointment does one of two things: it makes you 'bouncy' (resilient) or it makes you 'bitter' – and which one you end up is a more telling predictor of future happiness than 'rich' or 'poor', 'nice' or 'nasty'.

Bounceability is easy in your twenties. Underneath the veneer of sophistication most twenty-somethings are teenagers at heart

Here's an idea for you

Next time you're in the middle of a crisis, try to laugh every chance you can. And if you can't laugh, cry. One way or another vent your emotions. Your mind will work better when strong feelings aren't interfering with your ability to think straight.

convinced that their life is going to be fabulous. But during our thirties, the decisions we make pretty well determine what sort of person we're going to be, and how we decide to deal with setbacks is one of the greatest determinants.

Each of us is born, apparently, with a happiness set-point which is genetically influenced, but crucially, not fixed. However, what we learn from grumpy parents is likely to be a lot more influential than what we inherit genetically. We learn that life is fixed, that we can't change, that we're not in control. But that's wrong. The thing to remember is this: your brain chemistry is not fixed. You can change it.

How? When bad stuff happens, ask yourself what are known as 'coping' questions which challenge inflexible thinking. What would be useful for me to do right now? What is the reality, and what is merely my fantasy about this situation? Can I salvage anything from this?

Then ask yourself some 'serendipity' questions. Why is it good that this has happened? What am I learning from this? What could I do to turn this situation around?

Ultimately, what it comes down to is remembering that everything changes and change itself is the source of anxiety. Bad stuff happens to good people. But there are plenty of people who have had every disappointment in the book and still lived useful, happy lives. And before you mutter 'bully for them', science will tell you that there's no reason why you can't be one of the bouncers too.

22. Blitz your home in a weekend

Decluttering. Space clearing. Deeply relaxing.

Nothing makes you feel so serene and in control of your life as chucking out stuff you don't need.

How does it work? Most of us live among piles of ancient magazines, defunct utensils, clothes that neither fit nor suit us. The Chinese believe that all these unlovely, unwanted things lying about haphazardly block the flow of energy – the chi – in our homes. My theory is that by losing them, we lose a ton of guilt – guilt that we'll never fit into those hellishly expensive designer jeans again, guilt that we spent all that money on skis when we only go skiing once a decade, guilt that we never cook those fabulous dinners in those two dozen cookbooks. Cut your belongings by 90% and you do the same to your guilt.

Here's an idea for you

Try the 'one in, one out' rule. For instance, if you buy a new pair of shoes, then you must get rid of an existing pair. An added bonus is that this system protects you against impulse purchases of stuff you're not really fussed about as you have to focus your mind on what you'll chuck out when you get home.

'Useful or beautiful, useful or beautiful' – that's the mantra. If any single object doesn't fulfil one of these criteria, bin it. Cultivate ruthlessness. If you haven't worn it, used it or thought about it in a year, do you really need it?

Have three bin bags to hand as you work. One for stuff to chuck out, one for stuff to give to charity, one for things you want to clean or mend. Visit the charity shop as soon as you can – make it a priority. Give yourself two weeks to tackle the 'mend or clean' bag.

Something neither useful nor beautiful, but that you don't like to get rid of for sentimental reasons? Put it away for a year. Time out of sight makes it easier to get rid of.

Do this little but often. Try a couple of one-hour sessions per week. I operate the 40–20 rule: 40 minutes graft followed by 20 minutes sitting around feeling virtuous. You get better at decluttering. Soon it's second nature. Do two to three sessions a month. Find a home for everything you own. You're allowed one drawer that acts as a glory hole for all the odd items.

23. Iceberg!

Like the *Titanic*, you're beetling along coping like a trooper and then, *kerboom!* You're scuppered. You can't get out of bed.

That's the effect of iceberg stress. Most of it is hidden under the surface, and by the time we realise how bad it is, it's too late. There are always signs, but we rarely pay attention to them until they are dangerous. It's possible to go on for a long time with low grade stress symptoms. A very long time. The signs will be there, but are you paying attention?

Below are a few questions worth asking yourself. It will give you an idea of where you fall in the stress gradient, stage 1 being less difficult than stage 3. Those with stage 1 may be showing mild signs of iceberg stress, those with stage 2 moderate symptoms. Exercise, sleep, a decent diet and – most of all – changing your habits will do a lot to help. Those on stage 3 should consult their doctor and consider overhauling their lifestyle pronto. They almost certainly have iceberg stress.

Stage 1 – snowball
Do you often get minor skin blemishes such as cold sores?
Do you get cravings for sweet, sugary foods?
Do you experience energy slumps?

Stage 2 – snowman

Are you prone to spots that don't appear to be related to puberty or the menopause?

Do you get every bug going and find it hard to recover from illness?

Do you get constipation or suffer tummy problems such as bloating or acid reflux?

Are you inexplicably overweight?

Have you lost weight because you're just too busy?

Stage 3 – the whole damn iceberg

Do you suffer from exhaustion all the time?

Do you suffer from eczema that is getting worse?

Do you have irritable bowel syndrome that's not under control?

Do you suffer from high blood pressure, palpitations or dizziness?

24. Speed parenting

Children pick up adult anxiety like a dry sponge soaks up water.

Calm parents usually means calm kids, but when you're frazzled, they reflect it and have a horrible tendency to get bad tempered, argumentative, clingy and sick.

That's because nervous tension is contagious. You get stressed, your kids get tetchy – at best. At worst, they get ill. Most parents know the rule of 'reverse serendipity' that guarantees it's on the days when your car gets broken into and your job depends on you delivering a fabulous (and as yet unprepared) presentation that your youngest will throw a wobbly and hide under his bed refusing to go to school because he's dying.

Here's an idea for you

Write down your ten emotional highs in the last month and ten emotional lows. If it's easy to think of the bad times, but not the good ones, you may be more anxious than you realised. Feeling emotionally defunct is a sign that burnout could be closer than you think.

It's not mere coincidence. Research shows that even when they're tiny, children pick up on their anxious parents' frowns, tense jaws, averted eyes and other physical signs of worry. In turn, they cry or become withdrawn.

Short-term answer

Explain that you're under pressure, tell them why, but also show them that you're working out a way to handle it. Your competence in the face of an ultra busy day is an invaluable lesson for later life. Saying 'I'm stressed, here's what I'm doing about it', and giving them a timescale of when they can expect you to be back to normal goes a long way to reassuring them.

Here's an idea for you

Next time you talk to a child get on their level, eye to eye. They respond better. Kneel when they're toddlers. Stand on a stool when they're teenagers.

And on those days when it's all going pear-shaped, your kids are being unbearable and not letting you get on with what you have to do, then the best advice is to give them what they want – your time. This piece of advice was taught to me by a grandmother and I've been stunned at how well it works. Pleading for an hour of peace won't work, but ten minutes of concentrating on them – a quick game, a chat, a cuddle and a story – calms them down and they tend to wander off and let you alone.

Long-term solution

More than all the myriad advice I've had on childcare from child behavioural experts, the most useful was from a taxi-driver who told me that since his three children were born he'd always made a point during the working week of spending ten minutes a day with each one of them. Ten minutes a day sounds meagre but it's enough – if you actually do it. It's better to be realistic and consistent than to aim for an hour and achieve it only once a week. Even worse is to keep interrupting your time together to take a call from the office. Chat, wash their dolly's hair, read a story (hint: older children still like being read to) – but treat that ten minutes as sacred.

25. Never lose your keys again

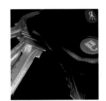

Often you can't remember where you left the car keys. Sometimes you can't remember where you left the car.

Memory lapses aren't necessarily the first indication of Alzheimer's, so don't worry. But if they're increasing in frequency it could be that your memory is a casualty of a multi-tasking lifestyle. This in itself causes great anxiety.

When you're very busy you're not taking in information in the same way and you're not going to be able to recall it. So be prepared. For example, on a busy day when you meet someone new, be aware that you are more likely to forget their name. Make more effort than usual during introductions. Repeat a new name inside your head. Use it again in conversation as soon as you can.

This repetition is important. When learning anything new during an anxious period, repeat it to yourself and if possible say it out loud three or four times, increasing the amount of time between each repetition. This 'repetition, pause, repetition' pattern strengthens memory.

Here's an idea for you

Try a supplement. There's some evidence that the herb gingko biloba improves blood flow to the brain and hence memory in the elderly, but it's likely that it will be proven to help younger people too. You can buy supplements containing gingko at chemists and health food shops. Sage is also good for memory.

This technique also works for items or tasks that you have to remember – and always forget. If you're fed up going to the supermarket to buy tomatoes and coming back with everything else but tomatoes, try the above. If it doesn't work, then make allowances and leave notes in your purse or on your toothbrush, places where you will certainly check. Don't rely on your memory.

Most routine actions will cause memory problems if you do them differently every day. The very fact that we do some things over and over again can make them easy to forget. That's because when you put items you use frequently in different places from one day to the next, you have to block the memory of what you did with them yesterday and the day before in order to find them today. Which is why it seems you've spent a half of your lifetime looking for your keys and wallet.

The easiest thing is to create a memory pot – a bowl or basket near your front door where everything goes as soon as you get home, and which you check before you leave the house. This isn't as simple as it sounds – it takes about two or three weeks before it becomes second nature. And even then, it makes sense to keep a spare set of keys somewhere separately.

26. Zap those piles

How to overcome the general detritus of 21st-century life that threatens to overwhelm you.

This is the system that works for me, culled from reading and interviewing just about every organisational guru on the planet. The only drawback is that it takes time to set up. But if you have a day to spend or ten free hours, give it a go. Ten hours can work magic. You will probably have to make a few adjustments to suit your life.

Step 1

Gather together everything that you will need to create order in your world. For me that's cardboard magazine holders, folders, pens, labels, stapler, a couple of hard-backed address books (personal and business) and a huge industrial-strength binbag. I also keep the family calendar and my diary at hand so I can put dates directly into them as I reveal the invites and school dates in my pile.

Step 2

Work systematically. You are going to go from one side of your desk to the other, or one side of the room to the other. Gather together one pile of paper and assorted junk and place it bang in the middle of the room or your desk. Start sorting. Every single piece of paper that you touch must be actioned.

- If it contains a phone number that you might need in the future, then put the number straight into one of your *address books.*
- If it is a bill that has to be paid, or anything which must be acted on immediately, then create a file for *urgent and unpaid bills.*
- If it is an article or piece of information that you might need in the future but which is not urgent, start creating files for these (*named files*) such as 'pensions', 'holidays', 'general interest'.
- If it is a piece of information that you need to act on or read or make a decision on but not now, put it in a file marked *'To Do'* and make an appointment in your diary sometime in the next week when you'll deal with it.

Keep a tickle book. Tickle as in 'tickle my memory'. I note down the names of anything I might need in the future: the idea of an article I might write or a savings account offering a good rate of interest. The point is that I don't have to hold on to endless bits of paper just in case I ever want this information – there's enough in the tickle book to help me trace it. I also keep the tickle book by my side at work and if anyone calls me with a piece of information I may need but don't know for sure, then I scribble down their number and a couple of explanatory lines so that I can follow up later.

Here's an idea for you

Chuck out files regularly: it's a good way to keep on top of paperwork. Every time you open a file, put a pencil mark on the corner of it. At the end of six months or a year, you'll be able to see in a moment which files you've barely opened. Most of their contents can be chucked out.

27. The clinic is open

If stress is affecting your health here's what to do about it.

Stress hits your hormones hard. And this can make its effects felt in the darnedest places…

If your digestive system is upset

Adrenaline slows digestion so food hangs around in your gut for longer, leading to constipation and bloating. Conversely, noradrenaline acts to open up the bowel, which leads to diarrhoea. That's one reason why irritable bowel syndrome (IBS), which is often stress-related, can manifest itself with apparently opposite symptoms.

Take action: Probiotic supplements boost the good bacteria in the gut and this will help combat the effects of the stress hormones. If IBS is a problem for you, there has been some progress in the last few years.

Skin problems

When you're stressed, your body diverts resources away from areas that don't contribute to its immediate survival – that means your skin. Stress also makes women produce more testosterone and that can lead to a break–out of spots at times of stress.

Here's an idea for you

Make a list of your top seven people. Think of how important your continued good health is to them. If you can't do it for yourself, those we love can be powerful motivation.

Take action: A multivitamin will help fill the gap in your nutritional needs, and if your skin is dry take a balanced omega 3 and 6 oil. If spots are the problem, your doctor can prescribe drugs that will help.

If you get headaches

Adrenaline is one of a group of chemicals known as 'amines' and people who get migraines are particularly sensitive to them.

Take action: The Migraine Association recommends that those who get migraines avoid another amine – tyramine. This is present in foods such as caffeine, chocolate, cheese and red wine. Eat these on top of the effects of stress and you are serving up a double whammy.

If your'e always tired

The hormones that regulate sleep include serotonin and melatonin – and both can be affected by periods of worry. Research in the USA has found that this is compounded in people who don't sleep particularly well. They have high levels of the stress hormone cortisol – which unsurprisingly keeps you alert. Not useful at bedtime.

Take action: People who are short of sleep get into a hopeless cycle. It is hard to sleep when you're bang in the middle of an anxious period. Sleeping tablets if only taken for a very short period at a time of crisis are not addictive – but should only be taken for a few days. What is more worrying is when after the period of anxiety is over, you still have trouble sleeping. Then you need to tackle the problem aggressively with your doctor.

If you're prone to weight gain

There's a link between stress and weight gain. Stress is thought to interfere with the action of insulin which regulates energy release. This could be contributing to a condition known as 'insulin resistance' which leads to weight gain along with an increased likelihood of other dangerous conditions such as diabetes.

Take action: A low-calorie diet per se won't help the problem much if you are still eating the kind of carbohydrates that cause big fluctuations in insulin release, mainly processed ones. What will help is limiting the carbohydrates that you do eat to healthy ones such as vegetables. Have some fruit and wholegrain bread and pasta – but don't overdo even these, healthy though they are. Stick to one or two servings of them a day and eat them with a little protein or fat, such as a few nuts or some yogurt with a piece of fruit or some cheese with your toast. This slows down the breakdown and thus insulin release into your bloodstream.

Ultimately, getting on top of stress will help with all these problems. If you are suffering health symptoms that you know are related to stress, it's more important for you than most to look for solutions that will help you.

28. How to make everyone love you

Take the moral high ground. You'll like the view.

We are approval-seeking missiles. From birth we seek the praise and validation of others. And this constant need for approval is the source of some of life's greatest difficulties. Unfortunately, success-driven behaviours don't always supply (hopefully) what we got from our parents when we were kids – the praise and the absolute certainty that we are fabulously loveable and important.

When we're still comparing ourselves with other people – what they have, what they do – we feel less equal than them. And that sets up a deep anxiety that is stressful and usually leads to you trying even harder to make other people realise your superiority. And one day you wake up and no one seems to like you much. Not even your kids. Especially your kids as they are the people on whom you probably act out your surreptitious 'inferiority/attempt-at-superiority' routine more than most. In fact, the success-driven behaviours that we embarked upon to win approval are likely to result in the direct opposite. People think at best you're a bit needy and pathetic and, at worse, you're a grade A pain in the backside.

What would Nelson do?

Here is my favourite trick. The minute I start to feel the stirrings of inferiority – whether it's that my boss is unhappy with me, my partner is fed up with me, friends don't phone any more, that I'm generally worthless, I stop and think 'What would Nelson Mandela do?'

He's my man. But for you it could be Jesus, the Dalai Lama, Oprah Winfrey, Batman. Create the fantasy of them reacting to the situation you're in – and then behave as your hero would.

Be a hero in your own life. You will stop feeling the need to act superior to stop you feeling inferior. You will speak to people straightforwardly, refusing to be intimidated by those you feel are 'superior' to you, declining to play the silly game of putting yourself on some weird pecking order determined by who has the biggest house, best job, bigger salary, more degrees, cleverer kids, thinnest thighs.

You will be a person walking confidently through life spreading grace and goodwill. You will love the world and it will love you right back.

Here's an idea for you

For the rest of the day, try treating everyone you meet with exactly the same warmth as you would your best friend. Smile when you see them, compliment them on their appearance, let them know how they are adding to your general well-being. When you answer the phone, smile. Let your 'thank yous' ring out loudly. Being kind to everyone from the postman to your partner seems to halve stress levels.

29. Lost your mojo?

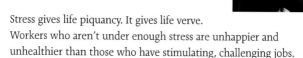

When you're bored, dull, lacklustre, you're as miserable as it gets.

Stress gives life piquancy. It gives life verve.
Workers who aren't under enough stress are unhappier and unhealthier than those who have stimulating, challenging jobs.

For challenge, read control. Because even though it seems a contradiction in terms, people under pressure tend to have more control than they realise. And that sense of control is so delicious that most of us go out of our way to bring more pressure into our lives, just so we can get the hit.

On the other hand, if your life is lacking in stress – or is quite challenging but you don't get any sense that you are in control – then you will get bored, frustrated and grim. You stop thinking you're a good person. You stop thinking you're successful. What they never tell you in all the reams about the evils of stress is that coping with it does wonders for your self-esteem.

Experts believe that our bodies are designed to be mentally and physically stimulated on a daily basis – whether it's running for the bus or meeting tight deadlines. When we put ourselves under pressure, we get rewarded for it. When forced to perform, our bodies release adrenaline. This triggers feel-good chemicals such as serotonin, which flood our body as a reward for completing a difficult task. Resolving a problem gives us a hormonal buzz and we feel terrific.

Here's an idea for you

Sit back and grin. You'll find a big smile sends the message to your brain to relax even when there's absolutely nothing funny happening.

If you're bored and fed up with life, you simply might not be stimulated enough. It's good to feel that you're competent, striving, achieving. In fact, I'll go further, it's impossible to feel this way without an element of stress unless you're an enlightened Buddhist monk. So if religion isn't your bag, it's imperative to find out what is. You might get your kick from being a Master of the Universe and killing the competition, you might get it from saving a wood of ancient oaks. You might get it from supporting your family without selling your soul. These are the big things, but little ones work, too. There are two important things to do:

1. Recognise what gives you a kick and seek it out

Next time you feel down in the dumps, don't head for the pub or turn to the biscuit tin. Get busy and up your achievement levels. Set yourself a goal to be completed by bedtime. Tidying your desk, cooking a perfect soufflé, making two calls you've been dreading.

2. Give yourself the space to enjoy the kick

After a completing any challenge, always, always, always switch off.
Remember you should either be relaxed or stimulated – not both at
once. If your body wants to rest after meeting a challenge and you
are full of anxiety about what you could or should be doing next,
'then your body doesn't know whether it is relaxed and repairing or
stimulated and solving', says stress expert, Liz Tucker.

30. What's your Plan B?

Take the insecurity out of your life. All you need is a Plan B.

The life you're living is Plan A. Plan B is what happens if it all goes
pear-shaped. Know how you'd get from A to B and you remove a
huge chunk of the stress caused by worry about the future.

Every life has its fair share of upsets and reversals of fortune. An
essential of the Plan B is to be able to look at your life
dispassionately and see potential fault lines – where your life is likely
to come apart. For instance:

- If you work in a volatile industry, it's work. Your Plan B is what you'll do if you are suddenly let go.
- If your relationship is struggling, your Plan B is what you'll do if you split up.
- If your health isn't good, your Plan B is to research methods of financing your life if bad stuff happens.

Here's an idea for you

Tomorrow open a completely new bank account for your Plan B. Start a direct debit and pay in until you've built up your emergency fund total of three months' living expenses. Knowing you've got enough money to finance your dream makes your present life a whole lot more fulfilling.

Plan Bs are brilliant for helping us relax. No one says you'll ever need Plan B but having one is invaluable comfort when you wake in the middle of the night and can't get back to sleep because of catastrophic thoughts swirling around in your brain. You know those nights? Well, with a Plan B, you worry for about 30 seconds, go 'Oh, I remember, I've got a plan B', roll over and doze off again.

For Plan B to work it has to be a fantasy built on reality. By that I mean it's not just a vague 'Oh, I'll sell the house and move to France.' It's more concrete than that.

First, decide on your Plan B and start a file. Add cuttings, pictures, information to it. Suppose you were going to sell your house and move to France. Your file for this would include information on people who had done the same thing, and research on how much you'd need to live on per year in France if you were mortgage-free.

Your Plan B should be realistic, but it should be inspiring _ training to become a chef, starting your own business, backpacking around Mexico. It should make your heart sing.

Think about the financial position you'd need to be in to make it work, and take steps to achieve it. The ideal sum for a 'just in case fund', whatever your Plan B, is eight months' worth of living expenses. Add up your outgoings for a year, divide the total by 12 to get your average per month and then multiply by eight.

Still reeling? Yes, it does have that effect. OK, eight months is ideal but it's that – an ideal. But if you want Plan B to have a relaxing effect build up at least three months' living expenses. That's the bare minimum that anyone should have easily accessible according to the experts.

31. Ditch the debt

Live on less than you earn. Hey, radical concept.

If you've tried to remove the source of your debt you might well be even more worried. Consolidating credit card debts into personal loans (at a lower interest rate) sounds like a good idea but it only makes matters worse if you carry on spending and don't deal with the original habits that got you into debt in the first place. (Hint: building up two debts is not the way to go.)

Here's an idea for you

Decide on an amount that you are allowed to spend each day. If by any chance you have any money left at the end of the day, stick it in a jar and save it. This too can become a bit of a game.

You've read it a million times before but here it is again. Get rid of credit card debt. There is no fast fix. It may well take you years. Move all your debt to a single credit card or two with 0% interest (and remember, these 0% deals may not be around for ever so don't think you can rely on them indefinitely to make the cost of your debt negligible). Check out the Saturday financial newspaper supplements for details of the best current deals. If you have a lot of debt, you will have to do this many times. Find out when your 'grace period' ends, and mark in your diary a month before you start paying interest. Start looking for a new deal then. Allow at least two weeks for the application to be processed and the transfers to be made, although internet banks are usually faster. Make sure you write to the old company cancelling your agreement and cut up the card.

How do you save more money?

Just writing down what you spend is enough to save money usually. But if you need 'special measures', try the following:

- List the stuff you absolutely have to spend money on to get to your workplace and function at your job – so that's fares and oh, all right, you can have a daily newspaper. No money for lunches (take in your own).
- Allow yourself discretionary spending money. Decide on a reasonable amount for the week – you'll know how much you usually spend each week from writing everything down – try halving that to begin with. Now you know what happens next. Go to the cashpoint and take out your basic times five, plus your discretionary – that's what you have to spend in a working week. You can spend the discretionary on what you like but when that's gone, it's gone.
- Use the principle of carrying only what you need at all times. Going to the pub? Estimate how many rounds you'll buy and how much they'll cost and yes, take that with you. When it's gone, you go home.

32. Take the tension out of your love life

Too wound-up to talk? Here's how to keep love alive.

This idea is the *sine qua non* of relationships. Once a week minimum, you and your partner have a 'date' where you focus completely on each other and nothing else. It may only be for a few hours. It doesn't have to involve a lot of money. You don't even have to go out – although I strongly recommend it.

Here's an idea for you

Get into bed. Whichever one is feeling emotionally stronger should 'spoon' around the other. Hold your hands entwined resting on the recipient's heart. Regularise your breathing so you exhale and inhale at the same time. Lie there and breathe in unison.

If you want something – ask for it. Second guessing what your partner thinks or feels is such a waste of time. You're nearly always wrong, and your assumptions lead to fights. You might assume your partner can see that you spending five hours a night on housework is unfair. On the other hand you might assume your partner can see that sex once a month isn't going to win you any prizes in a 'red-hot couple of the year' competition. (The two may well be related, by the way.) But you could well be assuming wrong. Work out what you want to make you happy. Then tell your partner. It might end up a compromise, but you've at least got a chance of getting it this way.

Keep surprising each other. No, not with the news of your affair with Geoff in accounts. To recreate the passion of your first romance, you have to see each other through new eyes. To do that you have to be passionate, engaged in your life, interested in the world. If you're not fascinated by your life, you can hardly expect anyone else to be. And remember the power of spontaneity. Plan to be spontaneous. Take it in turns to surprise each other, even if it's only with a curry – although the occasional weekend in Paris would be better.

A relationship that doesn't move forward will die. You have to dream big. Whether it's planning your next holiday, your fantasy house, another child, a downsize to the country. Not all these plans have to come to fruition, but you have to build common dreams and turn some of them into goals that you're working towards as a team.

Have sex

Call me old-fashioned, but I think having sex is important. Lots of couples don't of course, but I would say that unless you're both absolutely happy with this (are you sure? See first item on this list), then you're sitting on a potentially huge problem.

Giving your lover what they need to feel loved can melt away tension in a relationship. Find out what your partner needs to feel loved – meals out, compliments, sex, praise in front of your friends, jammy dodgers on demand. Ask. Then give it. Often. There is absolutely no use in you saying you love your partner, or showing them that you love them in your way, if they don't feel loved at the end of it. When your home life is unhappy, ask your partner. 'Do you feel loved?' And if the answer's 'no', do something about it.

33. Cherish yourself

Surveys show that we know exactly what we ought to do in order to relax. We just can't be bothered.

For the sake of research (and because a newspaper was paying me), I had every kind of relaxation therapy administered while hooked up to a heart rate monitor. Flotation and reflexology lowered my heart rate most.

Flotation

Floating naked in pitch darkness and utter silence for an hour at a time in heavily salted water isn't everyone's cup of herbal. Some flotation tanks now allow you to listen to music or have a small light burning throughout but I urge you at least to try the hardcore version unless you are claustrophobic. Sensory deprivation is the closest you can get to experiencing the security and comfort of the womb. After a while you become disorientated and that's when the magic happens. I know people who have had almost mystical experiences. Others have had the brightest ideas of their lives while floating. I've not had such an epiphany but I have felt relaxed and energised for days afterwards. A monthly or even better weekly float can really help.

Here's an idea for you

Try a quick stretch for instant relaxation. Sit facing a wall. Place your feet on the wall and bring your legs up so that the wall supports them. Edge closer so your backside is only inches from the wall. Lie still and breathe. Support the base of your spine with a cushion if necessary.

DIY version

Run a bath as deep as you dare. Empty one packet of Dead Sea Salts or Epsom salts (at least 500 grams) into your bath. Make the bathroom as dark as possible. Set an alarm clock for half an hour. Soak in the bath and sip herbal tea or water throughout to prevent dehydration. (Hot drinks increase perspiration, which is good.) Don't do this if you are pregnant, have high blood pressure, diabetes or any kind of heart problem. Don't dry off after bath, but wrap yourself in towels and go straight to bed. Be careful. You may feel light-headed. When you wake, have a warm bath or shower.

Reflexology

Reflexology is far more sophisticated than a mere foot rub – though that's not to be sneezed at. Having your feet cradled and massaged grounds you and is instantly calming. The theory is that all nerves originate in the spine and branch out through the body but ultimately all connect with the nerves that end in the foot. Each area of the foot therefore corresponds to an area of the body.

DIY version

First relax your feet in a foot bath into which you've added some tepid water and a few drops of peppermint oil. Then gently massage your feet using your thumb to make small circling movements over the whole sole of each foot. When you find a tender spot, work on it gently – this indicates an area where you have tension. Personally, I find rubbing the foot just below the little toe, just under the joint, relaxing. It corresponds apparently to the shoulders. Another place I've found it worth pressing (although I'm not sure it's strictly reflexology) is the furrow on the top of your foot where the bones of your first and second toes meet.

34. Runaway, runaway

Or to give it the grown-up name, retreat. Some time alone with your own thoughts is deeply relaxing.

This idea is about obliterating the low-grade noise pollution that is now the background for most of our lives. Televisions in every room. Telephones wherever you go. Music playing where it never played before (in the workplace, on the end of the phone while you wait). This constant barrage of noise is not relaxing. Here is a three-step plan to give yourself a break.

Here's an idea for you

Listen to some Bach, Chopin or Beethoven prior to falling asleep. It's been shown that people who listen to classical music in bed fall asleep more easily and sleep better than people who watch TV or listen to other sorts of music.

Step 1: switch off the TV

TV will eat up your life. Some 9-year-olds are watching up to four hours a day and these children perform less well on all measures of intelligence and achievement. TV does exactly the same thing to adults. It is such a very passive form of entertainment – it's been proven that just lying on the couch doing nothing burns off more calories than watching TV, presumably because at least you're generating some thoughts in your head.

Step 2: be silent

This is difficult to manage if you live with other people. But take a day off work and experiment with no noise. No TV, radio, no phone – switch it off.

Step 3: retreat

The best way of doing this is to go on a dedicated retreat – all sorts of institutions, religious or otherwise, run them. You can retreat and do yoga or dance or write or paint – or do absolutely nothing.

Of course, you don't have to leave home for that. It's much easier if you can escape but it's not impossible to put aside the hassles of everyday life and retreat in your own home. Clear away any clutter. Put away laptops, phones, diaries, PDAs – all work paraphernalia should be banished. Make your house as calm, restful and serene as possible.

Seven steps to retreating

1. Set aside at least 24 hours, preferably longer. Warn everyone you know that you don't want to be disturbed.
2. If you have family, do the best you can to escape. One way of doing it is to come back on your own a day early from a break, or leave a day after everyone else.
3. Get in all the food you'll need. Plan ahead. Make it especially tasty and nutritious. You don't want to have to venture out for supplies.
4. Switch off the phone. Don't open your mail.
5. Don't speak.
6. This is your opportunity to go inwards and not only relax fully but work out what you really want to do with your life. For that reason keep the TV and radio off. Listen to music if you like but make it classical and not too emotional. Limit reading to an hour a day.
7. Write in a journal, paint or draw, invent recipes. Do anything creative.

Better yet, be very still. Lie on the couch with a blanket and your thoughts. Breathe. Stay silent for as long as you can.

35. Can't get to sleep?

Depressed, fat, dead. You've got to sort this sleep thing out.

Facts: The most predictable predictor of depression is insomnia. Sleeping less than six hours a night is linked to increased obesity. Sleeping less than seven hours a night is linked to increased mortality. If you don't sleep well here are some key strategies:

- Don't drink caffeine for at least six hours before bed.
- Eschew alcohol and cigarettes for at least four hours before bedtime.
- Don't look at any sort of screen for three hours before bedtime.
- Get outside every day and do some exercise.

If this doesn't work...

Then the best advice is to think of yourself as a child. Infants are not born with the ability to soothe themselves to sleep, they need to learn it. You will have to re-learn the skill. You need consistency. A cast-iron routine that never wavers.

Stop all chores and any form of work at least two hours before bedtime. Develop a wind-down routine that starts about an hour before bed. Gentle yoga is brilliant for this, or you could lie on the sofa and listen to quiet music. Then run a hot bath. The bath is important. To counteract the heat your body lowers its temperature. Lowered body temperature triggers sleep. For that reason your bedroom and bed should verge on the cool. Cosy down in bed and read a book that isn't too thrilling and requires a little effort – Shakespeare's good, I find. Jane Austen is soothing. Do this every single night for a week.

Here's an idea for you

Try a 'power nap' for increased evening productivity. But if you're worried about feeling groggy when you wake, try drinking a strong coffee, then nap. It takes at least 30 minutes for the caffeine to kick in which gives you 30 minutes to doze.

If this doesn't work...

OK, let's get radical. You cannot sleep. You either can't get off to sleep or you wake early but you spend an inordinate amount of time tossing and turning. So don't. Just get up and do something else. See your insomnia as a gift. It's the chance to improve your life, to carve out some time for yourself. And before you dismiss this as utopian rubbish, a friend of mine found that within four months this tip had revolutionised her life. She used to go to bed at 11 p.m., wake at 4-ish and then lie awake until the alarm went off at 7 a.m., feeling miserable. So she started setting the alarm for 4.30 and getting up then instead. After a few days she discovered her optimal time was 5.30 a.m. She'd have a cup of tea and plan her day. She'd do a little work. A sleep expert advised her that sleeping only six hours a night wouldn't do her any harm at all if she managed a nap – humans are designed that way.

36. Have a holiday at your desk

Imbue the old nine-to-five with a certain glamour and you'll be amazed at how much tension seeps out of your life.

You can build a perfect day for yourself and by adding grace and glamour to your life, you will relax. It takes a little thought. But you can have a holiday of the 'mind' on even the most mundane day.

Reboot your commute

Give your journey to work an overhaul. Set yourself targets. Instead of a drag, see it as a purposeful part of your day. If it involves walking, buy a pedometer. Learn a language. Use the time to repeat your mantras for the day. Be creative: write a page of free-hand prose on the journey in. Start working up
the characters for your novel. The list is endless.

Boost your environment

Your starter question: what five changes would make your work environment more pleasant. Here's mine. Getting rid of piles of papers and magazines that need to be filed. Investing in a china cup and no more sharing the office's grubby, chipped ones. Cheering up my desk with a bunch of pink tulips. Cleaning my keyboard – so filthy it's a health hazard. Turning down the ringtone volume on my phone. Every day find some way to make your surroundings more pleasant.

Beat the mid-afternoon slump

When you feel the slump kicking in, stop working and get away from your workstation if you can. Go for a short walk in the sunshine, or take a nap. If you can't, try this: palm your eyes in your hands for a few minutes and visualise a calm and beautiful place. See this in as great detail as possible.

The journey home

This needs a different mood from the journey to work. If you listen to music, make it different from the tunes you play in the morning – slower, deeper. Small stuff like that really helps to emphasise that this is your transition period. Have a project that you work on at this time (planning your holiday is good). And if you read, keep the tone light. If in the morning you read French verbs or the novels of Dostoyevsky, read P.G. Wodehouse on the way home.

Spread love

When you pass someone in distress send them 'serenity' or 'calm' as a thought. Spread good and happy thoughts wherever you go. Smile. Be gracious. Be kind, compassionate, a force for good.

37. Perfect moments

The ability to create perfect moments is possibly the most valuable life skill you'll ever learn.

In the last few years, neuroscientists have moved their attention from what's going wrong in the brains of depressed people, to exploring what's going right in the brains of happy people. And for the most part, it's quite simple. Happy people don't get so busy worrying about building a 'perfect' tomorrow that they forget to enjoy this 'perfect' today.

It turns out that the surest, indeed, the only predictor of how happy you are going to be in the future is how good you are at being happy today. If you want to know if you are going to be happy tomorrow, ask yourself what are you doing to relax today? And if the answer's nothing, don't hold your breath. You won't be that calm and serene person you long to be any time soon.

I try to start each day with a perfect moment. When I wake just about the first thing I see is a bunch of fresh cut flowers. Then I read poetry for five minutes. I choose poetry because it reminds me that life is a lot bigger than me and infinitely more interesting.

But your perfect moment might be snatched late at night, listening to jazz by candlelight when the family are asleep. Or it could be a glass of chilled wine as the sun slips beyond the horizon. You might best be able to access a perfect moment by running round your park or through practising yoga. Listening to music while you exercise often heightens the sensations of being in tune with your body and tips you into joy. Preparing, cooking, eating food can give perfect moments. Gardening is a good one. Sex is reliable. We all know the sensation of feeling 'bigger' than ourselves. All you have to do is give yourself the space to feel it more often – ideally, at least once a day.

But ultimately, only you know your own triggers. Write down a week's worth and plan for them. Schedule them in your diary. Planning for perfect moments means they are more likely to happen. Even if you don't believe now that striving for perfect moments will relax you, try it. At least you will be able to say 'Today, there were five minutes where I stopped and enjoyed life.'

Here's an idea for you

Invest in an old-fashioned teasmade. Waking up to a cup of tea in bed can get the day off to a good start for little effort on your part.

38. Reach out

Touchy-feely behaviour is a good relaxation technique. Time to give love and, hopefully, get some back.

In general women are better at dealing with hassle than men. It's one explanation given for the fact that they tend to live longer. Research shows that although both males and females experienced the 'fight or flight' response, women have another way of dealing with anxiety – the 'tend and befriend' response. When women perceive danger their almost instantaneous reaction is to look after those weaker than themselves (classically, their children) and to reach out to others for comfort and support. This resulted in the release of the hormone oxytocin which is powerfully relaxing. So what can we learn from this?

Make friends People with friends of all ages – younger *and* older than themselves – tend to look younger and feel younger than those who restrict themselves to their own age group, and to be more relaxed. Social isolation is linked with poor survival rates in patients with coronary artery disease. Patients with three or fewer people in their social network were more than twice as likely to die as those with more people around them. We need *friends* – not just acquaintances. So it might be time to radically alter your attitude towards friendship. Look long and hard at your friendships – are they satisfying emotionally or have they been stale and just a bit boring for years. If you don't have a group of people who love, cherish and delight you – then seek them out, and this might very well mean seeing less of friends that you've already got

Volunteer Doing something positive for your community is a brilliant way of looking after yourself. A survey of volunteers discovered that around 63% reported that giving up their time to help others lowered their stress levels. (It also combated feelings of depression in around 50%.)

Get married OK, I'm being flippant. But people who are happily married are more relaxed than any other group. (Women who are unhappily married are among the most stressed.) Put time and effort into your relationship. If you want to relax, you need lurve.

Buy a pet Countless studies have discovered that having a cat or dog or other furry, friendly animal in your life can cause stress levels to plummet. One study even claims that cats purr on a frequency that is particularly relaxing for humans. If love is lacking in your life from other sources or is disappointing – get a dog or cat.

Here's an idea for you

When you're in the middle of an argument with a loved one, try this. Think about life from their point of view. What pressures are they under right now? Why do you think they are behaving in this particularly annoying way? Imagine love pouring from your heart to surround them in an imaginary hug. It's very hard to stay angry with someone when you begin to think gently of them and it can defuse blood-pressure-raising anger almost immediately.

39. Make life easy

Give up coffee, don't smoke, take exercise – we're always being told that unless we do our stress will become worse.

Without a doubt, one of the main reasons our bodies and minds are buckling under pressure is that our lifestyles are about as far removed from relaxation as it's possible to be.

Try one of these suggestions for a week or so, and when it's second nature add another.

Week 1

Drink a glass of water with every meal and every time you visit the bathroom. There are lots of smart alecs who will tell you we don't really need all that water. But water is almost unique in being a substance with no downside. It also gives you more energy.

Week 2

Swap one of your regular cups of caffeine for one healthy cuppa. Caffeine stimulates the adrenal glands to work overtime. It's been found that 4–5 cups of coffee a day raises stress levels by a third. Living on the adrenaline produced by tea, coffee, fizzy drinks and chocolate is just plain daft. I know. I did it for years. Redbush tea is brilliant. Unlike normal tea it is good for you – bang full of antioxidants but no caffeine. Unlike herbal tea, it tastes nice. Aim for no more than one cup a day.

Week 3

Eat breakfast every single day. Studies show people who eat breakfast are more productive –

Here's an idea for you

Start your day with porridge: the best calming breakfast is a bowl of the stuff. If you can throw in some yogurt or milk (for their stress-reducing nutrients) even better. Oats have been shown to keep stress levels lower throughout the day than other breakfasts and although muesli made with oats is good, cooking the oats as porridge works best.

and slimmer, incidentally – than those who miss it. I am not a breakfast person but again for the good of my health I forced myself to start eating within the first hour of waking up. This produces a huge difference in my concentration. Now I wouldn't miss it because I know the quality of my work is so much better.

Week 4

Every day eat…

- One orange – for vitamin C (or another helping of vitamin C-rich food).
- One helping of oats, fish, meat or eggs (for vitamin B, necessary for beating stress).
- One helping of broccoli or one helping of carrots – just brilliant for antioxidants.

At lunch. One small serving of good-quality carbohydrate. Too much and you'll feel dozy but one slice of wholegrain bread or a fist-sized portion of wholegrain pasta or rice will release the feel-good hormone serotonin.

Two to three servings of reduced-fat dairy, which is rich in natural opiates called casomorphins (have one serving with your evening meal if you have trouble sleeping).

At dinner. One small portion of good-quality protein (releases tryptophan which helps serotonin release).

This won't supply all the nutrients you need but it's a good start and it specifically delivers the nutrients you need to stay relaxed.

Week 5

Exercise. It is the single best thing you can do to lift your spirits and the best thing you can do for your health full-stop (with the exception of giving up smoking). Aerobic exercise (walking briskly, running, swimming) burns off excess stress hormones. Yoga lowers blood pressure in a matter of minutes, and after half an hour, relaxation levels have risen dramatically.

40. Standing tall

If your stomach hangs so low there's a chance of it keeping your knees warm, it's time for the Alexander technique.

The Alexander technique is a complementary therapy that quite literally leaves you walking tall. By working on your posture you enjoy a wealth of other health benefits – an end to back problems and less strain for starters. Those who practise the Alexander technique appear to grow taller, leaner and younger. Many believe that by improving our posture we also gain charisma, people take us more seriously and confidence levels soar.

The Alexander technique is so gentle it's quite difficult to know what is happening. A huge part of it is learning to hold our head in a relaxed way. The average head weighs about 5 kg (11 lb). Put five bags of sugar in a bag and try lifting it. Exactly. No wonder so many of us feel, literally, that we're carrying a huge weight on our shoulders. What the Alexander technique aims to teach us is something we once knew instinctively. Look at the perfectly arched back of your children and the heartbreaking grace with which they move: that's what you're aiming for.

The mantra is 'Relax. Float. Lengthen. Broaden.' Imagine your neck relaxing, your head floating, your spine lengthening and your

Here's an idea for you

Feeling tense? Think of your head as floating from your head like a balloon on a string. Imagining your head as light helps you to lengthen your neck and lift your head away from your shoulders automatically dispersing tension in the neck and shoulders.

shoulders and chest opening and broadening. Just repeating the words as you walk along helps.

Try this exercise for releasing tension. As you do it remember that the point is to allow your body to lengthen and widen. It helps to have this image in your head.

Lie down on your back on a rug or carpet for 10 minutes with your head resting on 5–7.5 cm (2–3 inches) of books and your knees bent so that your feet are on the floor but drawn up towards you. Your feet should be apart, to about the width of your shoulders. Rest your relaxed hands on your stomach. Imagine sinking down into the floor so that you feel tension draining from your back muscles. Let your shoulders release and 'melt' down into the floor. When you feel you've got the hang of this, tell your head to float away from your shoulders and feel your spine lengthen. Make no effort. Just use your mind and let gravity and your body weight do the job.

Perfect posture helps you to breathe better, and to walk gracefully and serenely through life. And when you're 5 cm taller (yes, I 'grew' 5 cm after doing the Alexander technique), life is far more relaxing.

41. You're not paranoid...they are out to get you

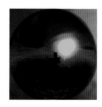

Are you ready for a journey to the weirder, wilder side?

I am just beginning to come out of a period of relatively high pressure. Here is the action plan that I drew up three months ago when this period started. (1) I phoned my lawyer and got him to deal with all the legal correspondence. Sometimes you need someone on our side. Assuming they're competent, there is absolutely nothing wrong with paying for it. (2) I was scrupulously polite at work, laboured extremely diligently and took pride in what I did, while formulating a Plan B. (3) I began exercising again – necessary to ground me. (4) I dug out a Tibetan prayer-ball that I keep for just such occasions, and I didn't leave the house without it for three months. A Tibetan prayer-ball is a pretty little bell that tinkles as you walk and it's believed to protect you against evil spirits.

You did what? I can almost hear the thuds as you throw this across the room but hold your fire. In terms of making me feel better, I think number 4 might have been the most useful of the lot.

Here's an idea for you

When you're feeling tense and under attack, mechanical repetitive tasks are good for centring you. Cooking works well; so does weeding the garden. Concentrate fully on your actions. Switch off your brain.

Here's the truth – sometimes the bastards *are* out to get you. I know all the arguments about wishing well to the world, good karma, turning the other cheek. I practise all of them. But sometimes through no fault of your own you become the scapegoat, the victim in life.

One of the simplest methods of boosting your ability to deal with bad karma is to build a shield around you. Sit quietly and find your still centre and then imagine a bubble of gold, silver or rosy pink enclosing your body and your energy field that surrounds your body – otherwise known as your 'aura' which you are more likely to be conscious of as your 'personal space'. Throughout the day remind yourself it's there and see the outside of this shield sparkling and fizzing with energy. On days when I face particular difficulties or concerns, I cover myself in imaginary psychic armour. (Practise this before you need it so it comes easily to you.) Breathe out your fear, breathe in courage. Sense a silvery metallic light filling your hands – this is liquid armour. Raise it over your head and smooth it over your body to encase your energy field. If you need more, scoop some up from a pool at your feet in one graceful motion and continue until you feel every part of you is covered in a completely flexible spiritual armour that will mirror back bad vibes. Say aloud, 'I am protected. No harm will I give, no harm will I receive.' At night mentally peel off your armour. Remember to be grateful for the protection.

42. Out of your head

**A way of relaxing that could improve your
sex life too. Result.**

Meditation is proven to reduce stress. I want to
be a meditator. God knows, I've tried. Like Vienna and elasticated
trousers it's something I'm looking forward to in my later years. In
the meantime, I will use an idea that delivers much of the benefits
without all the spiritual expectations, and is easy to bring into play
whenever you need it. A sort of meditation-lite, if you like.

Mindfulness came out of the work of Jon Kabat-Zinn, a scientist who
runs stress-reduction programmes at the University of Massachusetts
Medical Centre. Kabat-Zinn wanted to find a way of teaching patients
how to kick-start their own healing powers. Like meditation,
mindfulness gives control by helping you to listen to your body.

Lie down (although you can do this sitting if it is more convenient).
It helps at first to close your eyes. Become aware of your breathing.
Don't force deep breaths but 'see' in your mind your breath entering
through your nostrils and flooding your lungs. Listen to the sounds
of your breath. Concentrate on nothing else. When your mind
wanders, let these thoughts float away, imagine them as little white
clouds and return to the breath. (That's it.)

Here's an idea for you

Make your morning shower a mini-meditation session through the power of mindfulness. Listen to the sound of the water, and the sensation of the water on your skin. Let thoughts float down the plughole, concentrate only on what your body can feel, see and hear.

It's recommended you be mindful for 45 minutes a day for best results. If you can manage just 5 minutes (which is all I fit in most days), you will find it helps immensely. This keeps you calm when things gets hairy and seems to work especially well for maintaining your sense of humour when life seems dire. It appears to have all sorts of health benefits too – aiding healing and lowering blood pressure.

The point of this is to make you more aware of the here and now. It is quite shocking when you realise how often your mind is occupied with running over what has happened in the past and fantasising about what might happen in the future (and fantasy is all it is: none of us can know what's going to happen). The here and now is a great place to be – because nearly always in the here and now you are absolutely fine. Mindfulness transports you away from fear and towards self-reliance and self-confidence. You can use it when you're brushing your teeth. You can use it when you're having sex. It will automatically make any activity more profound and you more calm.

With practice you will find yourself falling into the mindfulness state at odd times – making dinner, crossing the road, in the middle of a conversation with your bank. This is the best way of turning 'space' into 'useful experiences'.

43. Supplementary benefits

Managing the strains of life is simply a matter of managing your body's chemistry. There is a whole battery of supplements that can help you do this.

If you have had a shock, or know that you are about to go through a very busy period – getting married, sitting exams – think about investing in a *B-complex supplement*. This supports the nervous system. Your body can't store B vitamins and has to replace them every day (which is also the reason you won't overdose on them, though of course it's sensible to follow the instructions on the bottle).

Stress affects your immune system and if you seem to be getting every bug going, you will probably benefit from an antioxidant supplement. *Vitamin C* is a powerful antioxidant that has been shown to help the body recover from shock faster. (When patients were given antioxidant vitamins following trauma or surgery the mortality rate was 44% lower among them one month later than in a group of patients not given antioxidants.) Consider taking a vitamin C supplement two or three times a day. Around 500–1000g

Here's an idea for you

Zinc is very good for combating the effects of stress. Look for a supplement that combines zinc with the main antioxidant vitamins A, C and E. This is a good one to reach for when you're really up against it.

in total should be enough; don't go over 2 g a day and don't take vitamin C if you have a history of kidney stones.

Always talk to your pharmacist before buying herbal supplements. Some interfere with prescription drugs. When it comes to herbal help, the best supplement to reach for is ginseng. It is one of the herbs that Russian scientists first dubbed the adaptogens – 'substances designed to put the organism into a state of non-specific, heightened response in order to better resist stresses and adapt to extraordinary challenges'. In other words, it helps boost performance, which is why athletes take it in the build up to a big competition.

How ginseng works is still unknown. It's thought it might affect the part of the brain called the hypothalamus, which controls the adrenal glands. By supporting the adrenals, it reduces the amount of stress hormones produced. Thus, ginseng minimises the effects of stress on your body. Herbalists recommend you take ginseng for no longer than three weeks without a break as it loses its effectiveness over time, but there are formulations that are designed to be taken all year round that clinical research has shown do some good in defusing stress and boosting energy.

Finally, there's another herb called rhodiola that is very good for helping you gain focus and concentration under difficult conditions. Students who took the herb for 20 days outperformed those taking a placebo, were less tired and felt more relaxed. You can buy it in supplement form fairly easily now, and like ginseng, if at all possible, start taking it a couple of weeks before a stressful period.

44. Love your money

And it will love you right back. When that happens life gets a lot more relaxing.

This idea is about respect. If you're disrespectful of your money, I'm prepared to bet that money is a worry in your life. If you don't take care of your money, the chances are that, just like a neglected teenager, it's never going to amount to much. Worse, the relationship will probably deteriorate further. One day your money is going to do the equivalent of coming home pregnant with a crack cocaine habit.

Here's a quick test

Get out your wallet or purse. Check out how it looks. Is it neat with bills folded, receipts tucked away. Or is everything stuffed in higgledy-piggledy?

Here's an idea for you

Go treasure hunting. Look for money down the side of sofas, in pockets, in foreign currency. How much money have you got stuffed in books. Or unrealised in gift tokens. How much of your money are you ignoring?

Here's a quicker one

How much money have you got in your wallet right now? If you're out by more than the price of a coffee, you need this idea badly. Your money is your friend. You should love it like a member of the family. You wouldn't go to the shops and forget to bring home one of the kids. Well, why the hell would you misplace your money?

Make a list of everything you spend in a day. Keep a notebook with you and write down how often you take money out of the 'hole in the wall' and what you spend it on. Every cheque you write. Every card you swipe. Every time you spend a penny. Literally. Keep it up for a week, preferably for a month. Now multiply (by 52 or 12). That's what it costs to run your life. Go through and highlight the big essentials – the mortgage, the essential bills. Now get out a calculator and work out what you spend on lunches, clothes, magazines, newspapers.

You're looking for what has been called 'the latte factor', those items that are completely expendable and add very little to your life but cost a fortune. It will frighten the bejasus out of you. My latte factor was £472. I needed that money a whole lot more than Starbuck's.

You also realise how much it costs to run your life. The very first day I practised this exercise I spent £197.45. And all I came home with was a pound of cherries. Shocking.

We're not going to talk about debt here but if you've got personal debt, do this for a month and you are going to work out exactly why.

45. Is stress making you fat?

Any sort of stress can lead to weight gain.

Stress causes your body to release cortisol and this stimulates the fat-storing hormone, insulin. Insulin causes your body to hold on to its fat stores. And that's if you're eating what you always ate. The trouble is that you might be sabotaging yourself without realising it. When we're anxious there's a tendency to overeat, especially carbohydrates. (It's not called comfort food for nothing.) That's because carbohydrates cause the brain to release serotonin and this is one of the feel-good hormones that raise mood. In a way, it's a form of self-medication.

Here's an idea for you

When you're anxious and feel the temptation to reach for comfort food, try sucking on half a teaspoon of honey instead (manuka honey from New Zealand is especially beneficial). Honey causes the brain to release the feel-good hormone serotonin almost immediately. You might find that just that tiny amount will satisfy you and prevent you pigging out on a bar of chocolate or a packet of biscuits which also cause serotonin release but pack a lot more calories.

Make a conscious effort to cut out salt

We can feel more drawn to salty foods when we're worried. There could be a physiological reason for this. Salt raises blood pressure and that in turn actually raises cortisol levels – which might have been an advantage when we only got stressed once a month but is redundant for the most part now. Wean yourself from adding salt to food and aim to eat no more than 6 g of salt a day in processed food. If the levels are given in sodium then multiply by 2.5 to get the grams of salt.

Get into green tea

Caffeine raises levels of stress hormones and makes you even more tense. Try green tea. It has about half the caffeine of coffee and a little less than black tea. And it's good for your brain and your circulation as well as your waistline. It's also thought that chemicals called catechins found in green tea trigger weight loss.

Savour food

Apparently, it takes 20 minutes for our stomach to register that we've started to eat and switch off the feeling of hunger. It's certainly borne out by a small US study of women who were instructed to eat slowly and stop eating when their most recent bite didn't taste as good as the first. They lost 3.6 kg (8 lb). In the same period of time, the control group gained 1.3 kg (3 lb). Our bodies know when we've had enough if we slow down long enough to listen.

Relax
One study showed that women who made a conscious effort to relax lost an average of 4.5 kg (10 lb) in 18 months without consciously dieting. The truth is you need actively to relax in order to switch off the stress hormones which could be contributing to weight gain.

46. How to love the job you've got

Sometimes you can't have the one you want. So you have to love the one you've got.

Hate your job? It's probably for three reasons – you hate the work, you hate the environment, including your colleagues, or something else has happened in your life that makes work seem meaningless and you're ready for a lifestyle change. The idea here will help you

Here's an idea for you

Boost work morale in a gloomy workplace by starting group traditions beyond getting drunk on Friday night and moaning. Go out for a Chinese on pay day or book an awayday at a spa or have a whip-round every birthday and celebrate with champagne and cake.

relieve stress in the short term and make you feel better about yourself in the long term. And that hopefully will help you raise your energy enough to eventually find another job.

Love your surroundings...

...Just as much as you can. If your workplace is grim you're not going to feel good. Clear your desk. Sort out clutter. Personalise your work space with objects of beauty and grace. Pin up photos of beautiful vistas you've visited or would like to visit. Change the visuals every couple of weeks or otherwise your brain stops registering them.

Love your lunch breaks

A lunch break shouldn't be a scramble for bad food and a desultory walk round a shopping centre. Spend time planning. Every lunch hour should involve movement, fresh air, delicious healthy food and at least one work of art. Always, always take an hour to relax at lunch.

Love your colleagues

If there are people who specifically annoy you, then find a way to deal with them. Allow yourself no more than five minutes a day unloading your woes about work colleagues to a trusted friend or partner – not anyone you work with.

Love yourself

Lots of people who are unhappy with their work kid themselves that they are working really hard, when in fact their work is shoddy and second-rate. If you're not up to speed, improve your knowledge base and skills. If your work is lazy, look at everything you produce or every service you offer and ask yourself how you can make it special, imbue it with your uniqueness, breathe creativity and a little bit of love into it. Doing every task diligently and with positivity will vastly increase your self-esteem.

Love your dreams

For five minutes in every hour allow yourself to dream. Read through job pages that aren't related to your present job. You may see a position or course that fires your imagination in a completely new direction.

47. Aromatherapy master class

Think that aromatherapy is just for wimps? Wrong. Aromatherapy has attitude. Aromatherapy kicks ass. Aromatherapy actually works.

Here's an idea for you

For days when you have to think fast, carry around a hankie with some peppermint oil sprinkled on it and sniff it to help you get focus. Studies have shown it aids concentration.

Aromatherapy is a bit of a joke. How often have you read 'sprinkle a little lavender oil in your bath to relax'? How often have you wondered how you'll find the time for a shower, much less a bath?

Let's face it, the people who can find the time to do the lavender oil stuff are probably quite relaxed already. And I thought so, too, until I interviewed Judith White, an inspirational aromatherapist who believes aromatherapy can do a lot more than make your bath smell nice. 'Aromatherapy is perfect for those times when you have only seconds because it works in seconds and it is one of the most valuable tools we have to help us live a less stressed, happier life,' she says. She speaks from personal experience. 'I had to learn how to keep myself on an equilibrium when my previous business left me emotionally, mentally and physically stressed for an extremely difficult few years. My oils were my greatest ally. That, and taking responsibility for the situation I was in.'

Judith is very hot on the idea that it is empowering for us all, but especially women, to accept that they are not victims, that they helped create problems in their lives and it's up to them to change their situation for the better. Think about the impact a woman's energy has within her home on her partner and kids. If a woman has a good day and her partner a bad one, he will soon be uplifted if she maintains her good spirits. On the other hand, if a man has a brilliant day, but the woman is down, then you will quickly watch his brilliant day evaporate as her energy dominates. Women have the energetic ability to sweep away everyone else's enthusiasm along with their own. Women's power over others is immense because we are the great intuitives and communicators and we can use these skills positively or negatively to affect others.

Look for opportunities throughout your day to stick in a mini multi-tasking treatment. Here are some I've found helpful. Oils aren't just for baths. When showering, cover the plughole with a flannel and add 4–6 drops (in total) of a combination of essential oils to the shower tray. Add one drop of essential oil to your existing moisturiser. Inhale deeply as you apply it. Try soaking your feet in an aromatic footbath while reading or watching TV. For an immediate treatment put a couple of drops of essential oil into the middle of a hot, wet flannel, wring it out, hold it over your face and breath deeply.

48. Burned out?

What is burnout? It's when a relationship – either work or personal – has got so bad that you just can't stand it any longer.

Answer these questions to see how stressed you are:

- You fantasise a lot about your perfect life that doesn't include your dull/annoying partner/job? +1
- You say 'I can't take it any more' at least once a week +2
- You feel unappreciated +3
- Tension is beginning to affect your health +3
- You wake up dreading the day ahead +3
- All you want to do in the evening is slump in front of the TV and sleep? +1

Score

4 or under = mild level of dissatisfaction. This indicates that the present situation is stressful but potentially saveable.
9 or under = life is not good and you know you need to act.
10 or over = burnout imminent.

If you have tried all you can to fix your particular hell and nothing improves, it's time to admit the unhappiness to yourself and others, and move on. The more time you've invested in the wrong life, the harder it is to give up on it. But the first step is simply admitting, you made a mistake.

Here's an idea for you

Spend 10 minutes every evening planning your next day. It's proven that you get one-fifth more work done if you review what you want to accomplish the next day in advance. Plus what you do achieve will likely be of higher quality.

Being unhappy with your life signals that you have outgrown your present situation and that it's time to move on. Otherwise, the strain of living a life that isn't yours can be fearsome. You risk burnout, which is extremely painful and can take months, even years to come back from.

But even if you do burn out, it's not an unmitigated catastrophe For many it's the beginning of a new more enlightened life. After spending their time in the metaphorical wilderness, they rethink their life and choose a new route.

Here's an exercise to help you get the process started:

- Lie down. Breathe deeply. When you're calm, ask yourself 'If I woke up and all my problems and worries had gone, how would I know a miracle had happened?'
- How would you behave, talk, walk, think – if the miracle had happened?
- How do you think your family and friends would know a miracle

had happened?

- If you were to assess your life right now somewhere between 0 and 10, with 0 being your worst life and 10 a full-scale miracle life, where would this day be on the scale?
- What would need to happen for you to move one step up?
- How would other people know that you had moved one step up?

This exercise helps you realise that it's not so much miracles (externals) that determine your happiness, but your behaviour. You are in control.

49. Happy holidays

Here's how to avoid falling ill every time you take a holiday.

The guy who first identified leisure sickness was a sufferer. Professor Ad Vingerhoets of Tilburg University noticed he always got ill on the first days of his holiday. So he did a study of nearly 2,000 men and women aged between 16 and 87. And guess what? He wasn't alone. Those who got it shared certain characteristics: a high workload, perfectionism, eagerness to achieve, an over-developed sense of responsibility to their work – all of which makes it difficult to switch off. So what can you do about it? Here's my two-pronged attack.

1. Support your local immune system

As a very bare minimum, eat at least five fruit and veg a day and take a good-quality multivitamin and mineral supplement. If you drink too much alcohol or are a smoker, you also need more vitamin C – so supplement that too.

2. Plan for holidays with military precision

You really need gradually to begin to wind down in the two weeks before you go. You think I don't understand, but I do. In August 1998, the day before my holiday, I worked in the office from 6 a.m. until 11 p.m., went home, packed, slept for three hours, went back to the office at 4 a.m., worked until 8.30 and took a cab straight to the airport to get on a plane. That's not smart. So let's have no more of the workaholic nuttiness.

Three weeks before you go. Make a packing list. Write down everything you need to take with you and then allocate each lunchtime this week to completing any errands.

Here's an idea for you

If you're prone to weekend sickness, try exercising on a Friday evening. Exercise is a stressor but one your body loves. This acts as a transition between work and time off, and helps you unwind quicker.

Two weeks before you go. Sort out work. Take a look at all your projects and decide at what stage you want to pass them over. Set goals with each project and allocate deadlines for reaching them preferably all to be tied up the day before your last day.

One week before you go. Start packing. Put out your bags or suitcases in a spare room if you've got one and start the washing and ironing nightmare in the weekend before you go. Do a little packing each night. Also start winding up projects and writing up your handover notes to whichever colleague is taking over your responsibilities. You can always amend them on the last day if you get further with a project than you planned to. Amending is a lot better than starting them at 8.30 p.m. on your last day.

50. Embrace the dark side

Reckon you're not an angry person?

Maybe that's why you're so tense. It's kind of obvious why screaming at people and being an antisocial creep is not relaxing. In its extreme form you end up in jail. But why does

suppressing anger make us
stressed? According to psychiatrist
Theodore Rubin, people attempt
to feel only those feelings that fit
in with their view of themselves.
But by doing this they put their
emotions in a deep freeze; they lose their capacity to feel all
emotions as acutely and the run the risk of living half a life.

Here's an idea for you

When you're upset, go to a quiet place
and have a good groan. Big theatrical
groans help to dissipate tension.

Anger is as valid as any other emotion, says Rubin. And it's one we
suffer from a lot. Psychiatrists believe we get angry every time we're
hurt or let down, but those of us for whom anger is a no-no learn to
pervert the anger into another emotion and it becomes anxiety,
bitterness or depression.

Once I went to an anger workshop to 'find' my anger. The leader was
a tiny red-haired woman. She told us that anger has to be expressed
both physically and verbally. She stood in front of a large beanbag (it
could have been a bed or a pile of pillows). She held a plastic baseball
bat in her hands. She centred herself in front of the beanbag, brought
the bat above her head and thwack! She banged the hell out of the
beanbag. She did it again and again. 'It's best to focus on the person
you're angry with,' she said calmly. 'Imagine they are the beanbag.'

That scared me. A lot. 'But you can't hit a person you're angry with,'
I squeaked. 'It's not a person. It's a beanbag,' she explained patiently

as to an idiot child. And of course, she's right. The anger is out and nobody gets hurt.

The idea is to thump and bellow your rage on the down swing. It takes practice. If you found it hard to find your voice, just concentrate on developing a rhythm. Let the feelings come in their own time. And they will. If you do this when you're angry, you'll defuse tension in a matter of minutes. You won't be such a nice person, but life will be a lot more straightforward. Once you start bashing out your anger, life gets a lot more fun. For one thing men with dodgy shirts don't have to be scared any longer.

51. Stop acting on impulse

Focus, concentration, sticking to what you've started. You will feel more positive instantly.

This idea will help you finish what you start, and this will make you feel in control of your life.

Step 1 Before you go to bed tonight, think of something you want to achieve tomorrow. Keep it really small and simple. Make it something restful – you're going to read a chapter of a favourite novel. Make it useful – you're going to clean the cutlery drawer. Make it worthy – you're going to take a multivitamin. Take this promise extremely seriously. Promise yourself you'll do it – and follow through. If you don't, no excuses. You've failed. But you're aiming too high. Make your next promise easier to achieve.

Here's an idea for you

Making a promise to yourself every night and keeping it the next day is the route to mental toughness. Every time you keep a promise to yourself, stick some loose change in a jar. It's a good visual record of your growing focus and strength – and, of course, you get to spend the cash at the end of it.

Step 2 Make a promise to yourself every evening for a week. And follow through.

Step 3 Make a list of some tasks that you need to undertake but have been putting off. One for every day of the week. Some ideas: starting on your tax return; making a dental appointment; cancelling the gym membership you never use; tackling just one pile from the many piles on your desk.

Step 4 Write these down and keep them by your bed. Each night for the next week, pick one and promise yourself you'll do it tomorrow.

Step 5 Write another list. This time put on it everything that is worrying you and driving you mad. Suggestions: discover if your pension plan will pay out enough for you to live on; write a letter to that friend you're upset with; paint the kitchen. Then pick one and break it down into manageable steps. Promise yourself to do the first of these steps tomorrow, and every day from now on, make a promise to take another step forward. Don't let impulse drive you off course.

This is an exercise in mental toughness. Making promises to yourself that you never keep brings you down and, over time, breaks your heart. But by breaking difficult tasks down into manageable chunks and building the strength of character to follow through and get them out the way, you take a huge step forward in reducing hassle in your life.

Warning: don't make more than two or three promises a day. Keep it simple.

52. Tame your lists

The problem with 'to-do' lists is that it takes seconds to scribble yet another entry – and a whole lot longer to get round to doing it.

What revolutionised the 'to-do' list for me was the idea of work days, buffer days and free days. Work days – self-explanatory. Free days – fun days and these should be a complete break from work. Buffer days act as a buffer against stress. These are the days you get on top of all those little things that need to get done – filing receipts, updating your CV.

Step 1 Prepare the master list. You need a notebook in which you write down everything that needs doing – now or in the future, important or unimportant. I know a fashion editor who has her special book of lists – a beautiful leather one in which she writes lists for everything – presents, places she wants to visit, books that she wants to read – as well as all the humdrum stuff. I like her book. It turns the 'to-do' list into a creative act.

Here's an idea for you

When you complete an item on your 'to-do' list, instead of putting a line through it, mark it through with a colourful highlighter pen. This raises your spirits and makes you feel you've achieved more. The more colour on the page, the more you've got through.

Step 2 OK, now you have your list, divide it into two with different coloured marker pens. One half will be stuff you have to do (insuring the car, buying your son a birthday present, finishing a work project), the other half will be the wish list, stuff you'd like to do in an ideal world (sorting out your photos, clearing out the cupboard you haven't looked into since 1987).

Step 3 Now get your calendar. You can use your diary, but a calendar works better. I like a big one with a month on a page. Mark out work days, buffer days and free days. Decide on the top five things on your 'must-do' list – some of these will be work, some will be buffer. Schedule these in on your calendar at the next appropriate session. I use three different coloured mini post-it notes, work, buffer and free. The colour allows you to see at a glance when your life is getting out of balance. It gives you an immediate visual reference of where you're spending your time.

Step 4 Look at your wish list. Pick three things on it. These will probably fall into buffer or free days. If you look forward to it with unalloyed pleasure, it's for a free day. If there is any element of duty whatsoever, it's a buffer. Scribble these on appropriate colour-coded post-it notes and bang them on the calendar. Every evening rip off the post-it notes for the next day and transfer them to your diary, sling 'em in the bin when you've completed them (which is very satisfying). And if you don't get something completed, take it home and find another slot for it on your calendar.

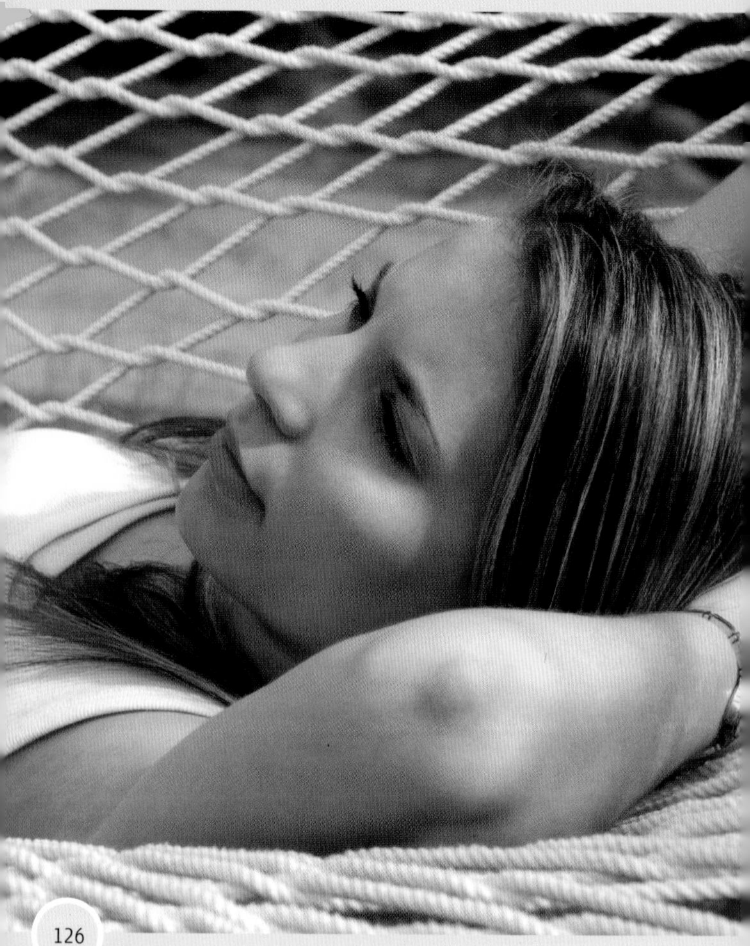

brilliant ideas

Relax: 52 brilliant little ideas to chill out is published by Infinite Ideas, creators of the acclaimed 52 Brilliant Ideas series. If you found this book helpful, you may want to take advantage of this special offer exclusive to all readers of *Relax*. Choose any two books from the selection below and you'll get one of them free of charge*. See overleaf for prices and details on how to place your order.

- **Downshift to the good life:** Scale it down and live it up
- **Healthy cooking for children:** 52 brilliant ideas to dump the junk
- **Inspired creative writing:** 52 brilliant ideas from the master wordsmiths
- **Look gorgeous always:** 52 brilliant ideas to find it, fake it and flaunt it
- **Re-energise your sex life:** 52 brilliant ideas to put the zing back into your lovemaking
- **Sleep deep:** Wake refreshed day after day
- **Upgrade your brain:** 52 brilliant ideas for everyday genius
- **Whole health:** Inspirational ideas for mind and body well-being

For more detailed information on these books and others published by Infinite Ideas please visit www.infideas.com

*Postage at £2.75 per delivery address is additional.

Choose any two titles from below and receive one of them free.

Qty	Title	RRP
	Downshift to the good life	£12.99
	Healthy cooking for children	£12.99
	Inspired creative writing	£12.99
	Look gorgeous always	£12.99
	Re-energise your sex life	£12.99
	Sleep deep	£12.99
	Upgrade your brain	£12.99
	Whole health	£12.99

Subtract £12.99 if ordering two titles

Add £2.75 postage per delivery address

Final TOTAL

Name: ....

Delivery address: ....

....

....

E-mail:...............................Tel (in case of problems): ....

By post Fill in all relevant details, cut out or copy this page and send along with a cheque made payable to Infinite Ideas. Send to: *Relax* BOGOF, Infinite Ideas, 36 St Giles, Oxford OX1 3LD. **Credit card orders over the telephone** Call +44 (0) 1865 514 888. Lines are open 9am to 5pm Monday to Friday. Just mention the promotion code 'RAD06'.

Please note that no payment will be processed until your order has been dispatched. Goods are dispatched through Royal Mail within 14 working days, when in stock. We never forward personal details on to third parties or bombard you with junk mail. This offer is valid for UK and RoI residents only. Any questions or comments please contact us on 01865 514 888 or email info@infideas.com.